Contents

Features

The *Maps: Read, Understand, Apply* series has been developed to teach important geography and social studies skills in four levels. Up-to-date, in-depth information in a self-contained format makes this series an ideal resource. Clear, concise maps present new concepts in a straightforward manner without overwhelming students. As students develop practical skills, such as map interpretation, they also develop the confidence to use these skills. The features incorporated into the series were developed to achieve these goals.

Two books make up the series:
Maps: Read, Understand, Apply, Grades 3–4
Maps: Read, Understand, Apply, Grades 5–6

Each book in the series is organized into four units. All units include a combination of teaching pages that introduce the skill and include practice pages, a review, and an application activity.

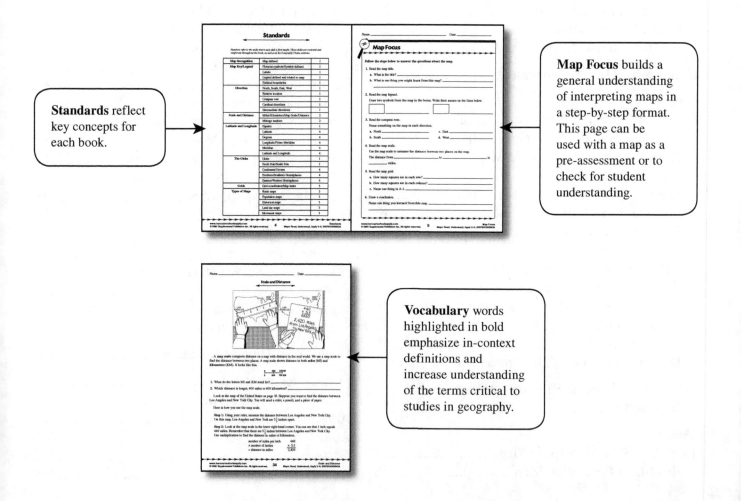

Standards reflect key concepts for each book.

Map Focus builds a general understanding of interpreting maps in a step-by-step format. This page can be used with a map as a pre-assessment or to check for student understanding.

Vocabulary words highlighted in bold emphasize in-context definitions and increase understanding of the terms critical to studies in geography.

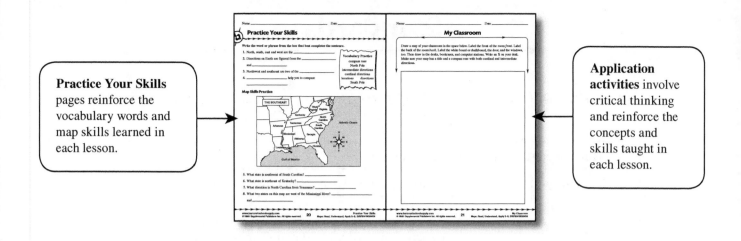

Practice Your Skills pages reinforce the vocabulary words and map skills learned in each lesson.

Application activities involve critical thinking and reinforce the concepts and skills taught in each lesson.

Introduction to Geography introduces the five themes of geography at the beginning of the book. This four-page feature provides definitions and questions that encourage students to think about the broad aspects of each theme.

Geography Theme sections further explain the five themes of geography. Each four-page section emphasizes the concepts and the relevance of the theme.

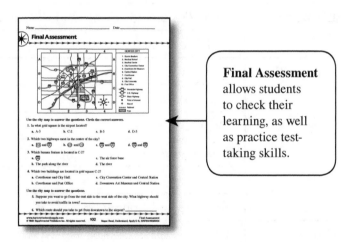

Final Assessment allows students to check their learning, as well as practice test-taking skills.

Atlas maps are a valuable reference tool for instruction and study.

The **Glossary** serves as both an index and a resource for definitions of key terms.

Standards

$\longleftarrow\longrightarrow$

Numbers refer to the units where each skill is first taught. These skills are reviewed and reinforced throughout the book, as well as in the Geography Theme sections.

Map Recognition	Map defined	1
Map Key/Legend	Pictorial symbols/Symbol defined	1
	Labels	1
	Legend defined and related to map	1
	Political boundaries	1
Direction	North, South, East, West	1
	Relative location	1
	Compass rose	1
	Cardinal directions	1
	Intermediate directions	1
Scale and Distance	Miles/Kilometers/Map Scale/Distance	2
	Mileage markers	2
Latitude and Longitude	Equator	1
	Latitude	4
	Degrees	4
	Longitude/Prime Meridian	4
	Meridian	4
	Latitude and Longitude	4
The Globe	Globe	1
	North Pole/South Pole	1
	Continents/Oceans	4
	Northern/Southern Hemispheres	4
	Eastern/Western Hemispheres	4
Grids	Grid coordinates/Map index	3
Types of Maps	Route maps	3
	Population maps	3
	Historical maps	3
	Land use maps	3
	Movement maps	3

Maps: Read, Understand, Apply 5–6, SV9781419099434

Name _____ Date _____

Map Focus

Follow the steps below to answer the questions about the map.

1. Read the map title.

   a. What is the title? _____

   b. What is one thing you might learn from this map? _____

   _____

2. Read the map legend.

   Draw two symbols from the map in the boxes. Write their names on the lines below.

   ☐ _____   ☐ _____

3. Read the compass rose.

   Name something on the map in each direction.

   a. North _____   **c.** East _____

   b. South _____   **d.** West _____

4. Read the map scale.

   Use the map scale to measure the distance between two places on the map.

   The distance from _____ to _____ is

   _____ miles.

5. Read the map grid.

   a. How many squares are in each row? _____

   b. How many squares are in each column? _____

   c. Name one thing in A-1. _____

6. Draw a conclusion.

   Name one thing you learned from this map. _____

   _____

5
Map Focus
Maps: Read, Understand, Apply 5–6, SV9781419099434

Name _____ Date _____

Introduction to Geography

In *Maps: Read, Understand, Apply* you will learn about some of the tools that scientists use to study **geography.** Geography is the study of Earth, its features, and the ways people live and work on Earth. There are five **themes,** or main topics, to help people organize ideas as they study geography.

The Five Themes of Geography
- Place
- Movement
- Human/Environment Interaction
- Regions
- Location

Geography Themes

◉ **Place** describes the kinds of features that make a location different from any other on Earth. **Physical features** are part of the natural environment. Some physical features are bodies of water, landforms, climate, soil, and plants and animals. **Human features** are developed or made by people. These features can include airports, buildings, highways, businesses, parks, and playgrounds.

1. As you study this illustration of a park, look for physical and human features. Use the physical and human features you find in the illustration to describe this park.

   _____

   _____

   _____

◉ **Movement** explains how people, goods, information, and ideas move from place to place. The movement of people from other countries to settle in the United States is one example of movement. Another example is trade. Goods move across the country or around the world through trade. The spread of information and ideas through the Internet is another kind of movement.

2. Name two ways that people, goods, information, and ideas move from place to place.

   _____

   _____

3. _____ **4.** _____

Both illustrations above show movement. On the line below each illustration, write *People/Goods* if movement of people and goods is shown. Write *Information/Ideas* if movement of information and ideas is shown.

◉ **Human/Environment Interaction** describes how people affect the environment and how the environment affects people. This theme also explains how people depend on the environment. For example, people depend on the land for good soil to grow crops.

Human/Environment Interaction demonstrates how people adapt to their environment. It explains how people make changes to live in their surroundings.

5. How do the people in this illustration adapt to the change of seasons in their climate?

_____

_____

_____

Name _____ Date _____

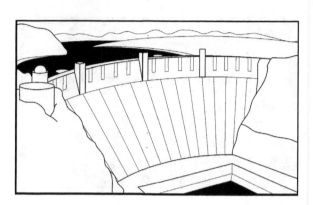

Human/Environment Interaction also describes how people change the environment to meet their needs and wants. Some changes may be harmful to the environment. For example, clearing land of all trees may cause soil erosion. Other changes made by people can be beneficial.

6. Look at the illustration of Hoover Dam shown here. How do you think changing the flow of a river's water might affect the plants and animals in the area?

_____

_____

_____

⊙ **Regions** name areas that share one or more features. Physical features, such as landforms, natural resources, or climate can describe regions. Appalachia is a region in the eastern part of the United States defined by its physical feature—the Appalachian Mountains. Human features, such as land use, politics, religion, or language can also describe regions. Regions can be large or small.

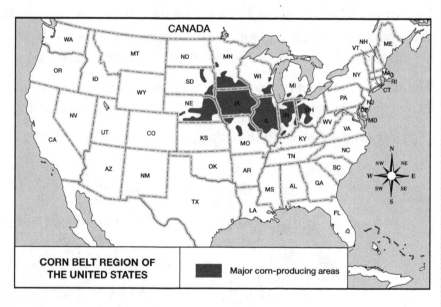

CORN BELT REGION OF THE UNITED STATES — Major corn-producing areas

7. Look at the map of the United States shown here. List the states that make up the Corn Belt. What makes the Corn Belt a region?

_____

_____

_____

Regions can be large, such as the Eastern Hemisphere, or small, such as a neighborhood. Canada is a region described by political divisions called provinces.

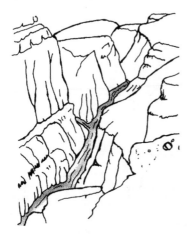

8. _____   9. _____

How would you describe the regions shown in these illustrations? List a physical or human feature that defines each region.

◉ **Location** describes where something is found. You can name a location by using its address. Another way you can tell the location of something is by describing what it is near or what is around it. Location helps us learn where a certain lake is found, or how far a person from Maine must travel to get to Idaho.

10. Look at this illustration. How would you describe the location of this home?

_____

_____

_____

_____

Name _____ Date _____

✦ Geography Theme: Place

Place is a location that has physical and human features that set it apart from other locations. Physical features can include bodies of water, landforms, climate, and plants and animals. Human features can include the kind of the government, customs, art, buildings, and other things made by people. The map below shows Florida and some of its features.

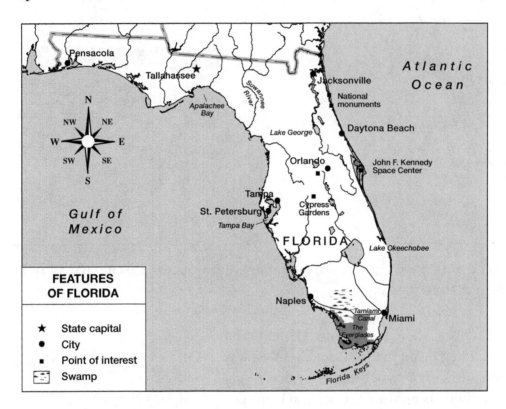

1. Big Cypress Swamp is one physical feature of Florida. This swamp is east of Naples, Florida. Use the symbol for swamp to find and label Big Cypress Swamp on the map.

2. Name three other physical features of Florida shown on the map.

   _____

   _____

   _____

3. The John F. Kennedy Space Center was set up in 1964 as a launch site for space missions. It is on the coast southeast of Daytona Beach. Circle this feature on the map. Then write **P** next to the circle if it is a physical feature. Write **H** if it is a human feature.

Maps: Read, Understand, Apply 5–6, SV9781419099434

Name _____ Date _____

Place focuses on the physical and human features of an area. Is the climate humid and wet or cold and dry? Are there mountains, hills, lakes, or valleys? How are the people governed? What language do they speak? The answers to these kinds of questions describe place.

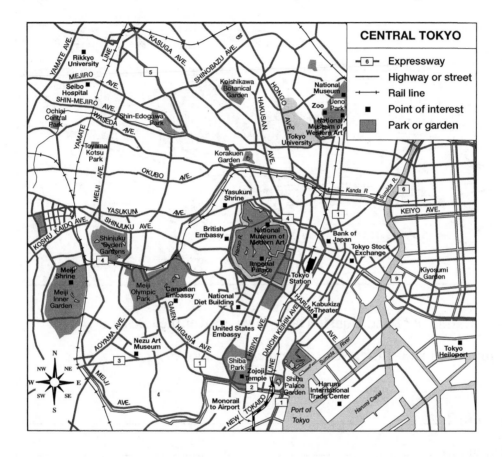

1. Based on the map, what are two physical and two human features of Tokyo?

   Physical feature 1 _____   Human feature 1 _____

   Physical feature 2 _____   Human feature 2 _____

2. Name a human feature that is in Tokyo because Tokyo is the national capital.

   _____

3. How do the features of Tokyo differ from those in your town or city?

   _____

   _____

Maps: Read, Understand, Apply 5–6, SV9781419099434

Look at the illustration of Grand Coulee Dam. Then answer the questions.

1. What are three human features you see in the illustration?

Human feature 1 _____

Human feature 2 _____

Human feature 3 _____

2. What are three physical features you see in the illustration?

Physical feature 1 _____

Physical feature 2 _____

Physical feature 3 _____

3. How do the human and physical features work together?

_____

_____

Name ———————————————————————— Date ————————————

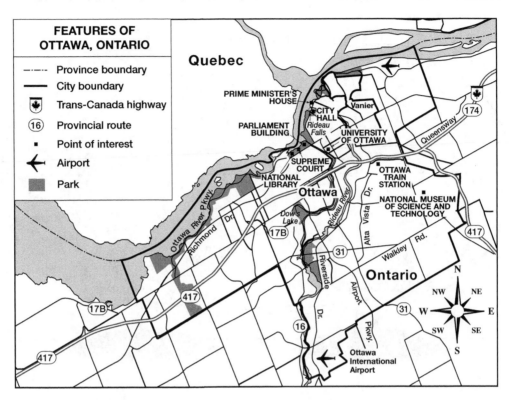

1. The Ottawa River forms the northwestern border of Ottawa. Label the Ottawa River. Then write **P** next to your label if it is a physical feature. Write **H** if it is a human feature.

2. Name two physical features of Ottawa. ——————————————————————————

——

3. What are four human features of Ottawa? ——————————————————————

——

——

——

——

4. Describe how the features of Ottawa differ from the town or city where you live.

——

——

——

Name _____ Date _____

Directions

←——————————→

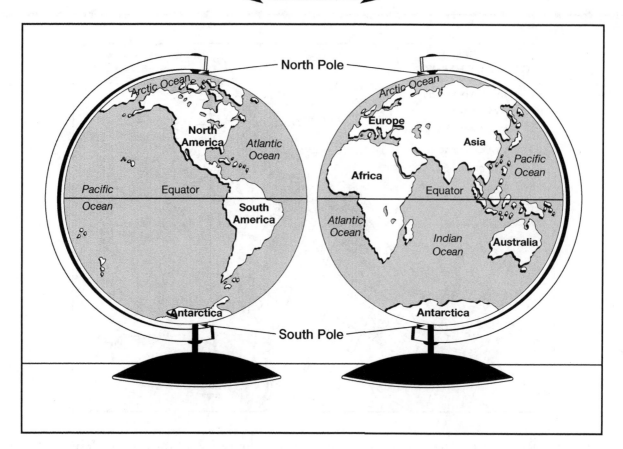

A globe is a model of Earth. Like Earth, a globe has the shape of a sphere, or ball.

The drawing above shows a globe. How can you find a place on the globe? One way is to show its **direction** or the notations that help compare location. North America is located on the northern part of the globe. North is the direction toward the North Pole. Find the North Pole on the globe above. The **North Pole** is the farthest point north on Earth.

The South Pole is at the opposite end of Earth from the North Pole. The **South Pole** is the farthest point south on Earth. South is the direction toward the South Pole. All directions on Earth are figured from the North and South Poles.

Two other directions are east and west. North (N), south (S), east (E), and west (W) are called **cardinal directions.** You know that once you are facing north, then east is always to your right. West is to your left. South is behind you. Knowing these directions will help you to find places. Practice using directions on the globe above.

1. South America is which direction from North America? _____

2. The Arctic Ocean is which direction from North America? _____

3. The Pacific Ocean is which direction from North and South America? _____

4. The Atlantic Ocean is which direction from North and South America? _____

Maps: Read, Understand, Apply 5–6, SV9781419099434

Name _____   Date _____

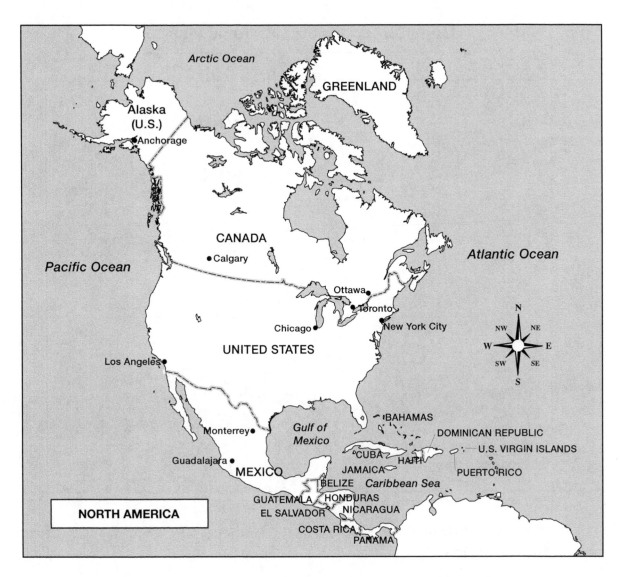

Maps have a special symbol to help you find directions. This symbol is called a **compass rose.** Look at the map above. Find the compass rose. North (N), south (S), east (E), and west (W) are all marked on the compass rose.

There are also other directions on the compass rose. These directions are in between the cardinal directions. They are called **intermediate directions.** The intermediate directions are northeast (NE), southeast (SE), northwest (NW), and southwest (SW). You need these to locate places that are between the cardinal directions.

Find Chicago on the map. Find Toronto. What direction is Toronto from Chicago? It is between north and east, or northeast.

1. Find Calgary on the map of North America above. In which direction would you travel from

Calgary to reach Anchorage? _____

2. From Monterrey, what direction is Guadalajara? _____

3. From Los Angeles, what direction is Monterrey? _____

Name _____ Date _____

Using Directions on a National Map

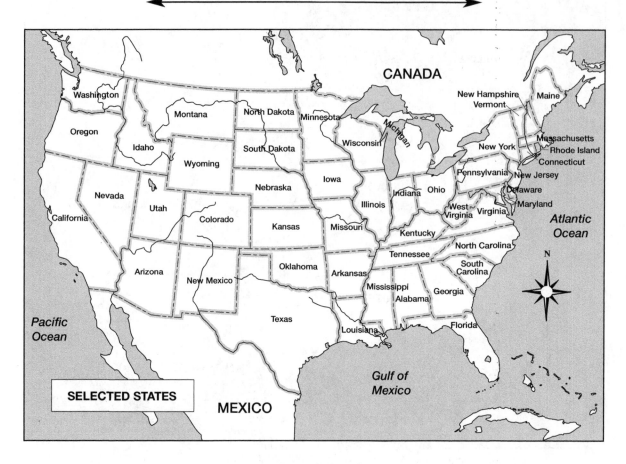

SELECTED STATES

1. Complete the compass rose on the map above. Add the missing cardinal directions. Then add the intermediate directions.

2. Find Kansas on the map. Circle the label.

   a. Which state is north of Kansas? _____

   b. Which state is south of Kansas? _____

   c. Which state is east of Kansas? _____

   d. Which state is west of Kansas? _____

3. Which state is northeast of Utah? _____

4. Which state is southeast of Arkansas? _____

5. Which state is southwest of Illinois? _____

6. Which state is northwest of Iowa? _____

7. What is west of California? _____

8. What is southeast of Texas? _____

Maps: Read, Understand, Apply 5–6, SV9781419099434

Name _____   Date _____

Using Directions on a Regional Map

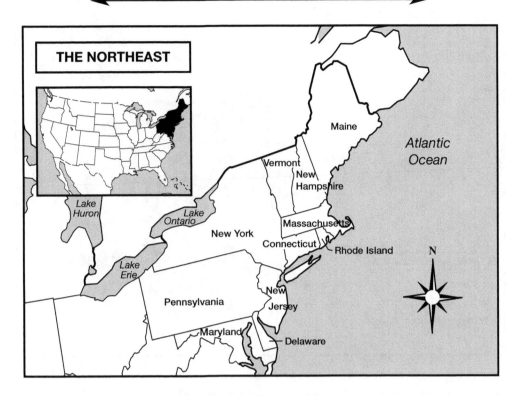

THE NORTHEAST

Maine

Atlantic
Ocean

Lake
Huron

Lake
Ontario

Vermont
New
Hampshire

New York

Massachusetts

Connecticut

Rhode Island

N

Lake
Erie

Pennsylvania

New
Jersey

Maryland

Delaware

1. Complete the compass rose. First add the cardinal directions. Then add the intermediate directions.

2. Write a direction to make each sentence true.

   a. New Hampshire is _____ of Massachusetts.

   b. Pennsylvania is _____ of New York.

   c. New Jersey is _____ of Connecticut.

   d. New Hampshire is _____ of Rhode Island.

   e. Maine is _____ of New Hampshire.

3. Draw a conclusion. Find the small map of the United States above. It shows where the Northeast region of the United States is located. Why do you think this region is called the Northeast?

   _____

   _____

Name _____ Date _____

Using Directions on a National Park Map

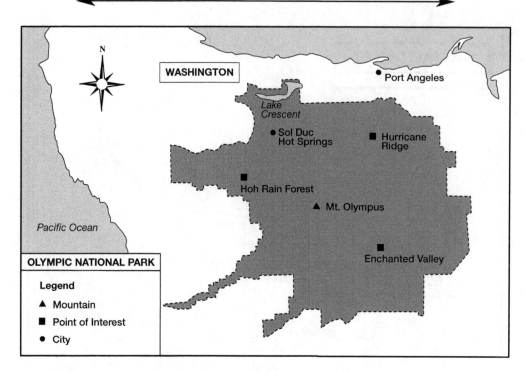

You are going on a camping trip through Olympic National Park in the state of Washington. You will be hiking and do not want to get lost.

1. Complete the compass rose.

2. Your trip begins at Hurricane Ridge. It is in the northeast part of the park.

   a. Circle it on the map.

   b. What direction would you look to see Mt. Olympus? _____

3. You will hike to Lake Crescent from Hurricane Ridge. What direction will you be walking?

   _____

4. From Lake Crescent you will hike to Sol Duc Hot Springs. What direction will you be going?

   _____

5. You want to camp in the Hoh Rain Forest. What direction do you hike from Sol Duc Hot

   Springs to the Hoh Rain Forest? _____

6. What direction is the Pacific Ocean from the Hoh Rain Forest? _____

7. Your last stop will be at Enchanted Valley. It is in the southeastern part of the park. What direction will you travel to get back to Hurricane Ridge from Enchanted Valley?

   _____

Name _____   Date _____

Mastering Directions on a Map

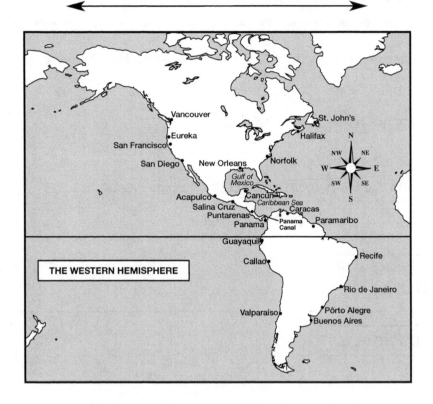

THE WESTERN HEMISPHERE

1. Write the following labels where they belong on this map.

    NORTH AMERICA   SOUTH AMERICA   CENTRAL AMERICA
    ATLANTIC OCEAN   Equator   PACIFIC OCEAN

2. Plan an ocean cruise along the western coast of North America. Begin in Vancouver. Name, in order, four other port cities on your route. _____

    _____

3. Sail from the western coast to the eastern coast through the Panama Canal. What body of water do you enter? _____

4. Continue sailing south along the eastern coast of South America. Name, in order, four port cities along this route. _____

    _____

5. Trace your route from Vancouver to Buenos Aires in red. Circle the cities on the route.

Name _____ Date _____

Practice Your Skills

Write the word or phrase from the box that best completes the sentence.

1. North, south, east and west are the _____.

2. Directions on Earth are figured from the _____

   and _____.

3. Northwest and southeast are two of the _____.

4. _____ help you to compare

   _____.

Map Skills Practice

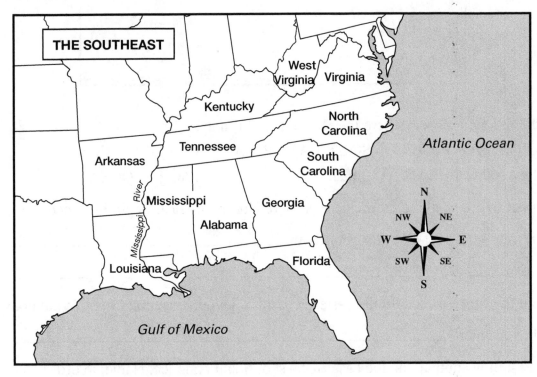

THE SOUTHEAST

5. What state is southwest of South Carolina? _____

6. What state is northeast of Kentucky? _____

7. What direction is North Carolina from Tennessee? _____

8. What two states on this map are west of the Mississippi River? _____

   and _____

My Classroom

Draw a map of your classroom in the space below. Label the front of the room *front*. Label the back of the room *back*. Label the white board or chalkboard, the door, and the windows, too. Then draw in the desks, bookcases, and computer stations. Write an **X** on your desk. Make sure your map has a title and a compass rose with both cardinal and intermediate directions.

Maps: Read, Understand, Apply 5–6, SV9781419099434

Name _____ Date _____

Symbols and Legends

←——————————————————————→

A **symbol** on a map represents something that is on Earth. Symbols can stand for cities, mountains, or natural resources. To find the meaning of a symbol, read the legend. The **legend** explains what every symbol on the map means. We use the symbols and the legend to learn from the map.

Look at the legend above. Find the symbol for a state boundary. A **state boundary** shows where one state ends and another begins. Find a state boundary on the map.

Find the symbol for an international boundary in the legend. An **international boundary** shows where one country ends and another begins.

1. Find your state on the map. What is the state capital? _____

2. What states border your state? _____

3. What are the capitals of these states? _____

4. Does your state have an international boundary? _____

   If so, what country shares a border with your state? _____

5. What countries border the United States? _____

Name _____ Date _____

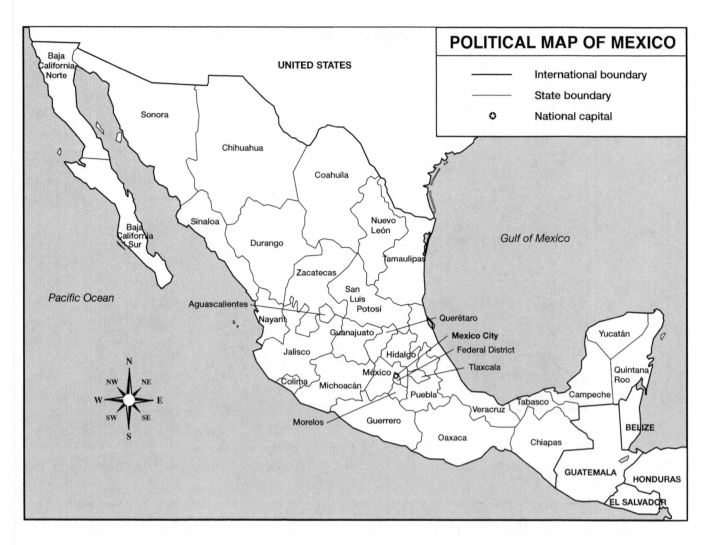

Some maps show special information about a place. **Political maps** show the boundaries separating states and countries. Other maps may show yearly rainfall or where people live. That is why the title is so important. The **title** tells you the purpose of the map.

Look at the title of the map above. It is a political map of Mexico. What can you expect to learn from this map? You can expect to find capital cities and state and international boundaries. The country of Mexico has 31 states. Like the United States, it has a national capital. Find the symbol for a national capital on the map.

1. What city is the national capital of Mexico? _____

2. What country touches the northern international boundary of Mexico? _____

3. Name two Mexican states along this boundary. _____ and

_____

4. List two Mexican states that border the state Colima. _____ and

_____

Name _____ Date _____

Understanding Symbols and Legends

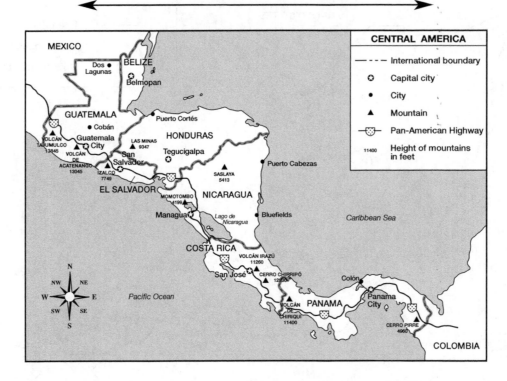

Not all maps show the same information. The title tells you the kind of information you can learn from the map. The legend explains the special symbols used on the map. The map above has several symbols.

1. Read the map title. What part of the world is shown on this map? _____

2. Read the legend. What major highway is shown on this map? _____

3. Read the legend. What kind of landform is shown? _____

4. Read the compass rose. Where is the North Pole from Central America? _____

Notice on the map above that the labels are not all the same size. Labels for the largest places on a map are usually large and sometimes are shown in all capital letters.

5. What countries make up Central America? _____

_____

6. The Pan-American Highway crosses which countries? _____

_____

7. a. Which country has the highest mountains? _____

   b. How high are these mountains? _____

8. Which mountain is located farthest east in Central America? _____

Maps: Read, Understand, Apply 5–6, SV9781419099434

Name _____ Date _____

Mastering Symbols and Legends

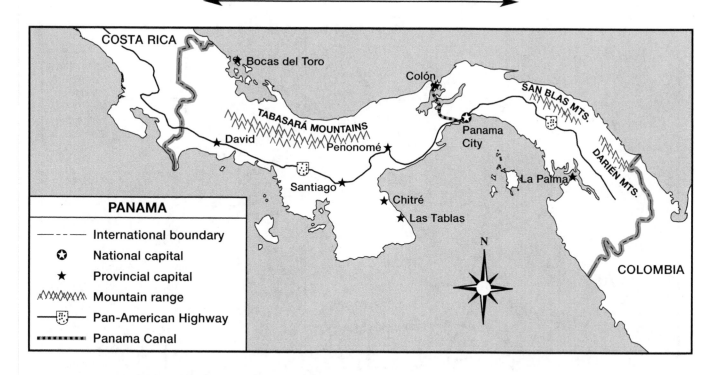

1. Read the map title. This map shows _____.

2. Read the map legend. What symbols are shown in this legend? _____

_____

_____

3. Read the compass rose. Find north. Label the remaining points.

4. Label these bodies of water. Look at the map on page 24 for help.
   Caribbean Sea   Pacific Ocean

5. What country borders Panama to the east? _____

6. What country borders Panama to the west? _____

7. How many mountain ranges are shown on this map? _____

8. List the provincial capitals shown on this map. _____

_____

9. Is the Pan-American Highway north or south of the mountain ranges? _____

Name _____ Date _____

Understanding a Political Map

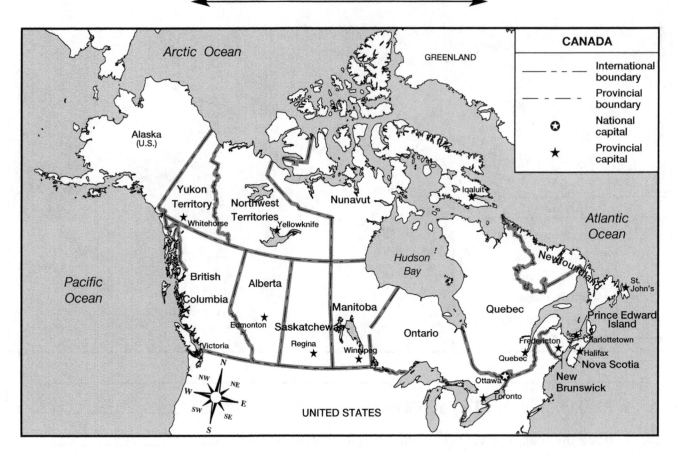

1. Canada is divided into ten provinces and three territories. The border lines look like state borders. Why is the border different between the Yukon Territory and Alaska?

_____

2. Circle the capital of Saskatchewan. Write its name. _____

3. Trace the borders of Saskatchewan in red.

   a. Which province is west of Saskatchewan? _____

   b. Which province is east of Saskatchewan? _____

4. What is the national capital of Canada? _____

5. Halifax is the capital of _____.

6. Iqaluit is the capital of _____.

7. What is the capital of the Northwest Territories? _____

8. What is the capital of the Yukon Territory? _____

Name _____ Date _____

Reading a Political Map

←――――――――――――――――→

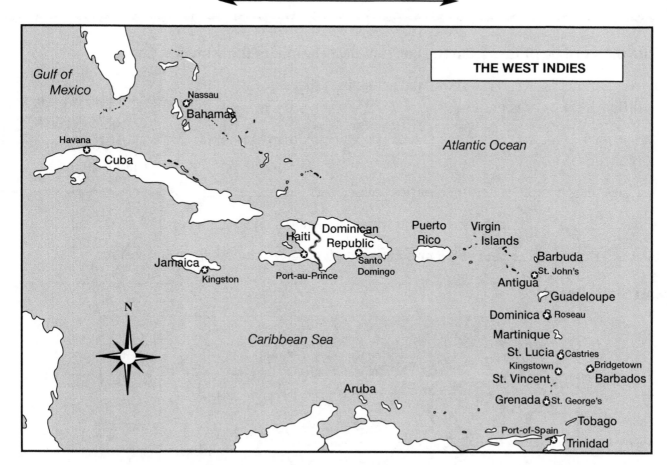

1. Label the compass rose with the missing directions.

2. Find the island that is divided into two separate countries. Circle this island. Name each country and its capital.

   a. _____

   b. _____

3. Locate the Bahamas on the map above. Nassau is the capital city of the Bahamas. Draw a line south from Nassau to the bottom of the map. What countries do you cross?

   _____

4. Write the intermediate direction that makes each sentence true.

   a. Martinique is _____ of Barbados.

   b. Trinidad and Tobago are _____ of Puerto Rico.

5. Draw a conclusion. The West Indies form the northern and eastern boundary of what sea?

   _____

Maps: Read, Understand, Apply 5–6, SV9781419099434

Name _____   Date _____

Practice Your Skills

Write the word or phrase from the box that best completes the sentence.

1. A _____ shows the boundaries that separate different states or countries.

2. The map _____ tells you what the map is about.

3. Lines that separate states or countries are _____.

4. The _____ tells you what the symbols on a map mean.

5. A _____ on a map can stand for a city, a mountain, or a resource.

Vocabulary Practice

symbol   legend
title   boundaries
political map

Map Skills Practice

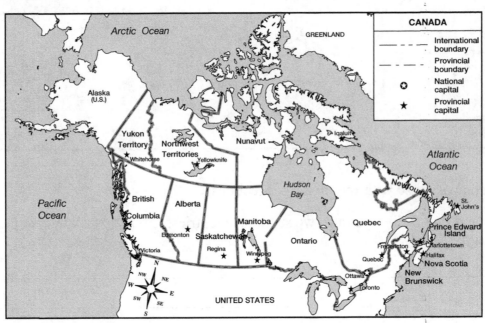

Match the capital with the province.

6. _____ Toronto   **A.** Manitoba

7. _____ Edmonton   **B.** Ontario

8. _____ Winnipeg   **C.** Quebec

9. _____ Quebec   **D.** Nova Scotia

10. _____ Victoria   **E.** Alberta

11. _____ Halifax   **F.** British Columbia

Practice Your Skills
Maps: Read, Understand, Apply 5–6, SV9781419099434

Name _____ Date _____

Locations in the News

Use a current newspaper to find three places mentioned in the news. Locate these places using the atlas maps on pages 104–106. Write the names of the three places on the lines. Briefly describe what newsworthy event is happening in each place. Then describe the locations of these places from your home or city.

Place 1

a. _____

b. What is happening in this place? _____

_____

c. Describe the location of this place from your house or city.

_____

_____

Place 2

a. _____

b. What is happening in this place? _____

_____

c. Describe the location of this place from your house or city.

_____

_____

Place 3

a. _____

b. What is happening in this place? _____

_____

c. Describe the location of this place from your house or city.

_____

_____

Geography Theme: Movement

Movement describes how people, goods, information, and ideas move from place to place. Movement shows people interacting. It demonstrates **interdependence,** or how people depend on one another to meet their needs and wants. The St. Lawrence Seaway is a waterway that connects the Atlantic Ocean with the Great Lakes. This waterway lies in Canada and in the United States.

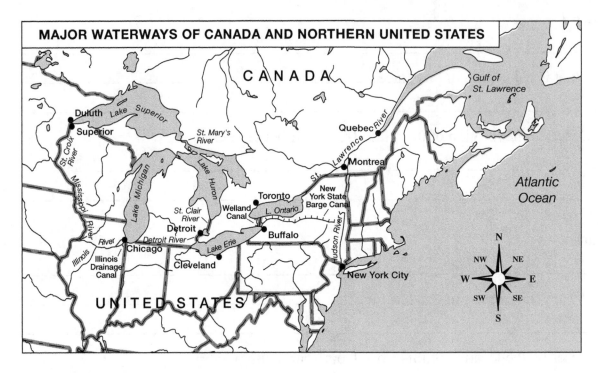

MAJOR WATERWAYS OF CANADA AND NORTHERN UNITED STATES

1. Trace the route of a ship that travels from the Atlantic Ocean into the Gulf of St. Lawrence, through the St. Lawrence Seaway, and to the Mississippi River.

2. What major bodies of water does this ship pass through?

_____

_____

_____

_____

3. What cities would the ship pass on its way to Chicago?

_____

_____

Name _____ Date _____

Movement describes the ways that people, goods, information, and ideas move from place to place. How do you get to and from school? Where do goods that you buy come from? How do you know what is going on in your community and in other parts of the world? These kinds of questions are answered in the study of movement. Movement happens through transportation and communication.

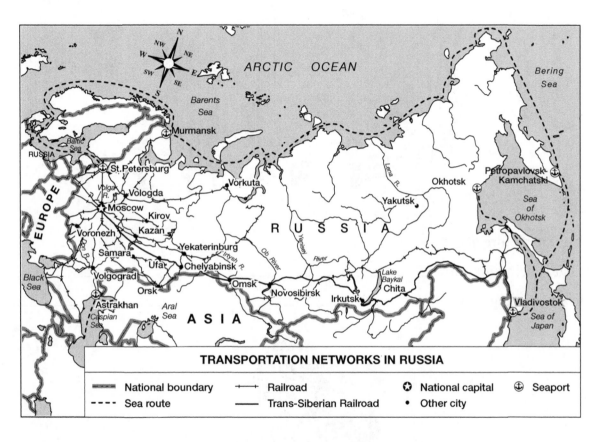

1. What transportation networks are shown on this map of Russia?

_____

_____

2. According to the map, how do people in Murmansk get goods to Vladivostok?

_____

_____

3. What means of transportation connects Russia's east coast with its western border?

_____

Movement can describe how people get from one place to another. People move from place to place in cars, trains, and airplanes. Movement also tells how people in a community depend on people in other communities for goods and services.

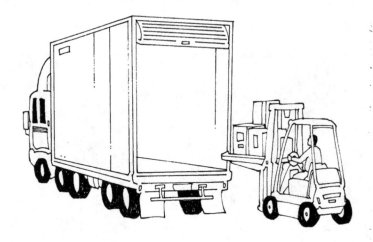

1. Look at the picture above.

   a. What is being moved? _____

   b. How is it being moved? _____

2. Look at the picture above.

   a. What is being moved? _____

   b. How is it being moved? _____

Maps: Read, Understand, Apply 5–6, SV9781419099434

Look at the map of Springtown. Answer the questions.

1. What are two kinds of transportation routes in Springtown?

_____

_____

_____

_____

2. What are three ways ideas move in this community?

_____

_____

_____

_____

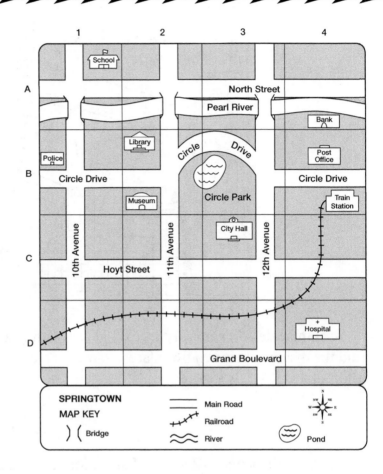

3. Mrs. Phuong is at the museum. She needs to go to work at the school. What route will she take?

_____

_____

4. Goods have arrived at the train station for the hospital. What route should the hospital worker take to pick up the goods from the station?

_____

_____

Scale and Distance

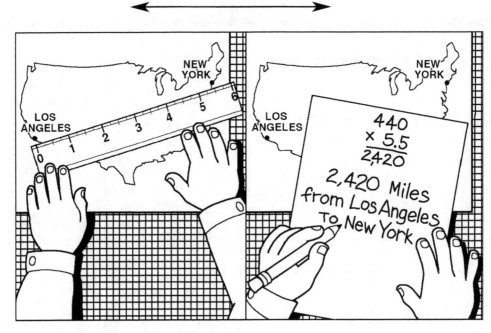

A **map scale** compares distance on a map with distance in the real world. We use a map scale to find the distance between two places. A map scale shows distance in both **miles** (MI) and **kilometers** (KM). It looks like this.

0	220	440 MI
0	350	700 KM

1. What do the letters MI and KM stand for? _____

2. Which distance is longer, 400 miles or 400 kilometers? _____

Look at the map of the United States on page 35. Suppose you want to find the distance between Los Angeles and New York City. You will need a ruler, a pencil, and a piece of paper.

Here is how you use the map scale.

Step 1: Using your ruler, measure the distance between Los Angeles and New York City. On this map, Los Angeles and New York are $5\frac{1}{2}$ inches apart.

Step 2: Look at the map scale in the lower right-hand corner. You can see that 1 inch equals 440 miles. Remember that there are $5\frac{1}{2}$ inches between Los Angeles and New York City. Use multiplication to find the distance in miles or kilometers.

number of miles per inch	440
× number of inches	× 5.5
= distance in miles	2,420

   Maps: Read, Understand, Apply 5–6, SV9781419099434

Name _____ Date _____

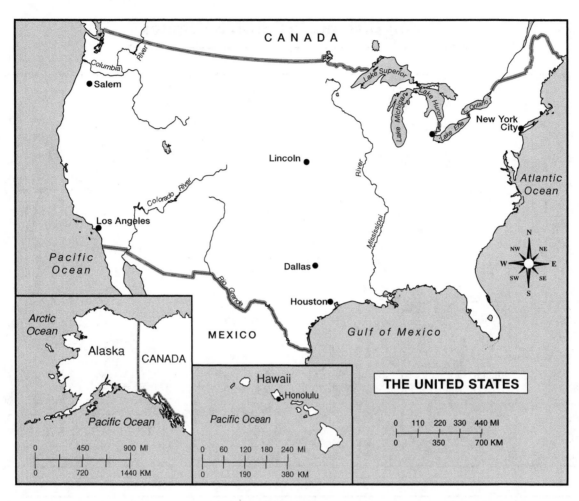

Look at the map of the United States above. Find the two smaller maps in the left-hand corner. One shows Alaska and the other shows Hawaii. Alaska and Hawaii are far from the other 48 states. This map is not big enough to show where Alaska and Hawaii really are. So they are shown in inset maps.

An **inset map** is a small map within a larger map. An inset map may have its own scale. Map scales change depending on how much area is shown. Compare the map scales on the inset maps with the large map.

1. One inch equals how many miles on the map of Hawaii? _____

2. One inch equals how many miles on the map of Alaska? _____

3. What can you tell about the sizes of Alaska and Hawaii? _____

4. To figure the distance between Dallas and Houston, which map scale do you use?

_____

5. What is the distance between Dallas and Houston? _____

6. Can you figure the distance between Honolulu and Los Angeles using these maps? _____

Why or why not? _____

_____

Name _____ Date _____

Finding Distance in the United States

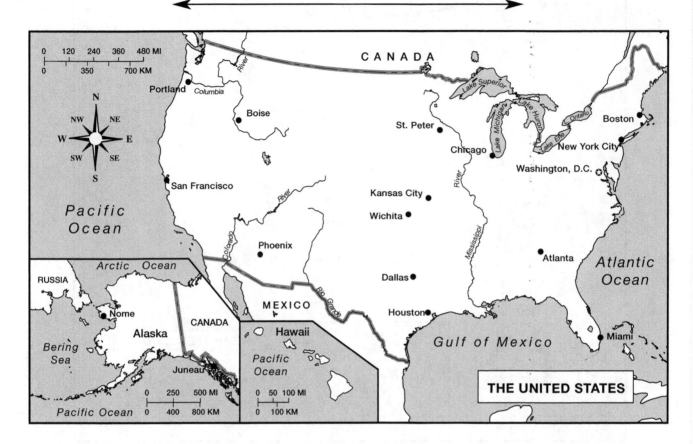

 1. Read the map title. This map shows _____.

2. Read the map scale. On the large map, one inch stands for _____ miles.

Use your ruler to figure these distances.

3. What two states are shown in the inset maps above? _____ and

_____

4. From Phoenix to Kansas City is about _____ miles.

5. From New York City to Washington, D.C. is about _____ miles.

6. From Kansas City to Boston is about _____ miles.

7. From Nome to Juneau is about _____ miles.

8. Is it farther from San Francisco to Houston or from Portland to Chicago? _____

_____

Name _____ Date _____

Finding Distance on a State Map

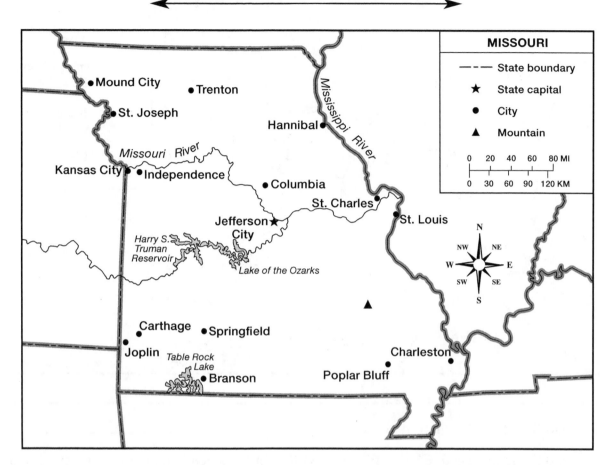

Imagine you are going on a tour of Missouri. Use a ruler to draw lines as you figure these distances and directions.

1. Find the state capital on the map. Circle it.

2. a. What direction will you go from the state capital to Springfield? _____

   b. From the state capital to Springfield is about _____ miles.

3. a. What direction will you go from Springfield to Carthage? _____

   b. From Springfield to Carthage is about _____ miles.

4. a. What direction will you go from Carthage to Poplar Bluff? _____

   b. From Carthage to Poplar Bluff is about _____ miles.

5. There is a mountain about 80 miles southwest of St. Louis and about 60 miles northwest of Poplar Bluff. Find it on the map. Label it *Taum Sauk Mountain.* You have reached the highest point in Missouri!

Name _____   Date _____

Finding Distance in Libya

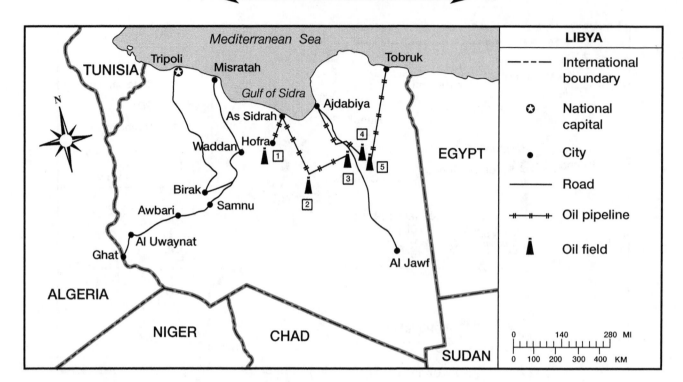

1. Read the title. This map shows _____.

2. Read the map legend. Check (✔) each symbol in the legend and a matching symbol on the map.

3. Read the compass rose. Complete the compass rose.

4. Read the map scale. The length of the scale stands for how many miles? _____

   How many kilometers? _____

5. Trace each oil pipeline. Then find its length.

   a. Hofra to As Sidrah   about _____ KM   about _____ MI

   b. Oil field #2 to As Sidrah   about _____ KM   about _____ MI

   c. Oil field #4 to Ajdabiya   about _____ KM   about _____ MI

   d. Oil field #5 to Tobruk   about _____ KM   about _____ MI

6. Which oil pipeline covers the longest distance? _____

7. Draw a conclusion. Where do all the oil pipelines in Libya go? _____

   Why? _____

Name _____ Date _____

Finding Distance in Southern Africa

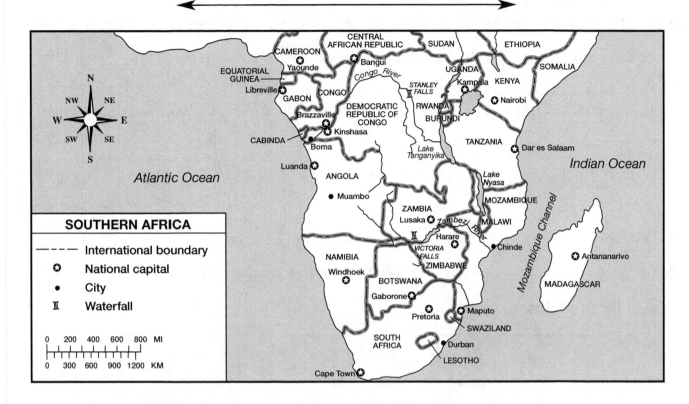

1. Draw a line from the first place to the second. Then find the distance.

   a. Cape Town to Windhoek   about _____ KM   about _____ MI

   b. Windhoek to Kinshasa   about _____ KM   about _____ MI

   c. Kinshasa to Bangui   about _____ KM   about _____ MI

   d. Bangui to Kampala   about _____ KM   about _____ MI

   e. Kampala to Nairobi   about _____ KM   about _____ MI

   f. Nairobi to Maputo   about _____ KM   about _____ MI

   g. Maputo to Cape Town   about _____ KM   about _____ MI

2. What is the total distance of this trip?   about _____ KM   about _____ MI

3. Trace the Congo River from Stanley Falls to Boma. Use the map scale to estimate this distance.

   about _____ KM   about _____ MI

4. Trace the Zambezi River from Victoria Falls to Chinde. Use the map scale to estimate this distance.

   about _____ KM   about _____ MI

5. Which river trip is longer? _____

Name _____ Date _____

Practice Your Skills

Write the word or phrase from the box that best completes the sentence.

1. To show the relationship between the actual size of a place and its reduced size on a map, mapmakers use

   a _____.

2. Distances in the United States are usually measured in

   _____.

3. Distances in countries other than the United States are usually measured in _____.

4. An _____ is a smaller map within a larger map.

Map Skills Practice

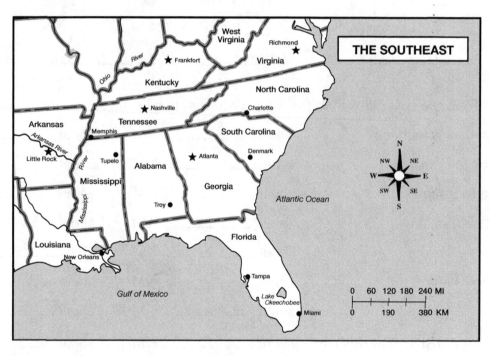

Use a ruler and the map scale to figure these distances.

5. From Atlanta to Richmond is about _____ miles.

6. From Memphis to Frankfort is about _____ miles.

7. From Nashville to Miami is about _____ miles.

8. Is it farther from Nashville to New Orleans or from Nashville to Richmond?

_____

Name _____ Date _____

Distances in My School

Work with a partner to determine the distance, in meters and feet, from your classroom door to the doorway or entrance to three important places in your school. Draw a map of your school in the space below, using symbols to represent each of the different places within your school. Your map should include a title, scale, compass rose, and legend.

Maps: Read, Understand, Apply 5–6, SV9781419099434

Name _____ Date _____

Route Maps

←――――――→

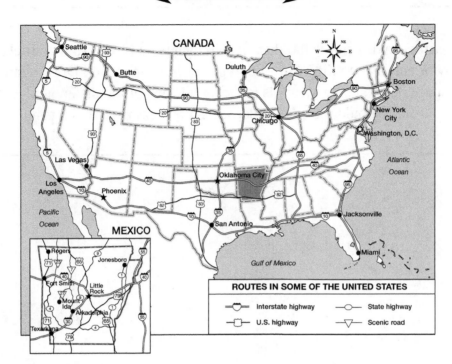

Some maps help us to plan a trip. The map above shows several kinds of routes. A **route** is a way of getting from one place to another. Each kind of route is shown in the legend. Find the symbol for an interstate highway in the legend. **Interstate highways** usually cross the country from one side to the other. Find an interstate highway on the map.

A **U.S. highway** crosses several states. Find the symbol for a U.S. highway in the legend. Then find a U.S. highway on the map.

State highways connect cities and towns within one state. **Scenic roads** cross areas that offer a beautiful view. Find the symbols for state highway and scenic road.

A **junction** is a place where two highways cross or meet. Put your finger on U.S. highway 20 in Chicago. Slide your finger to the left. What is the first U.S. highway you cross? Where highways 20 and 83 meet is a junction.

An **interchange** is a special kind of junction. An interchange is a place on a major highway where cars can get on or off the highway. Interchanges have special connecting ramps to allow vehicles to change roads without interrupting the flow of traffic.

1. Look at the inset map of Arkansas. What kinds of routes do you see? _____

_____

2. Interstate 35 connects what northern city with what southern city? _____

_____

3. What state highway crosses southern Arkansas? _____

Maps: Read, Understand, Apply 5–6, SV9781419099434

Name _____ Date _____

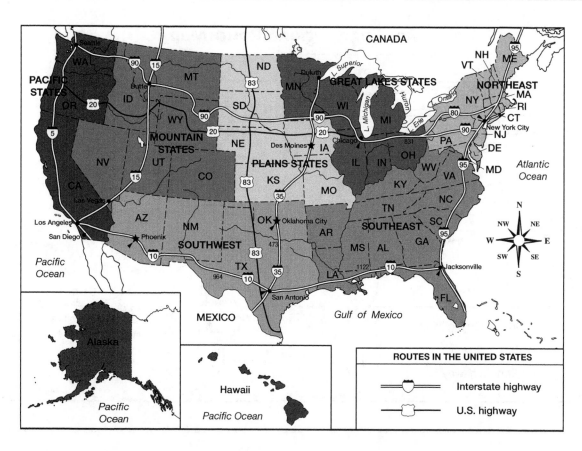

Look at the route map above. It shows interstate and U.S. highways crossing regions of the United States. A **region** is an area with many things in common. Find the Pacific States. Notice that all of the Pacific States touch the Pacific Ocean. What states are included in this region?

Three regions are named for intermediate directions. Find them. Name the states in the Southwest, the Southeast, and the Northeast.

Three regions are named for land or water forms. Find them. Name the states in the Mountain States, the Plains States, and the Great Lakes States.

Route maps often show the distance between cities. Find the small triangle pointing to Chicago. That triangle is a **mileage marker.** The next mileage marker east of Chicago is in New York City. The distance from Chicago to New York City is 831 miles. Find the small number 831 near the route from Chicago to New York City.

1. What lakes border the Great Lakes States? _____

2. What regions does Interstate 10 cross? _____

3. What is the distance from San Antonio to Jacksonville? _____

4. What interstate crosses the Mountain States from north to south? _____

5. What U.S. highway crosses the Plains States from north to south? _____

6. What highways would take you from Seattle to Las Vegas via (by way of) Butte?

_____

Maps: Read, Understand, Apply 5–6, SV9781419099434

Name _____ Date _____

Reading a Regional Route Map

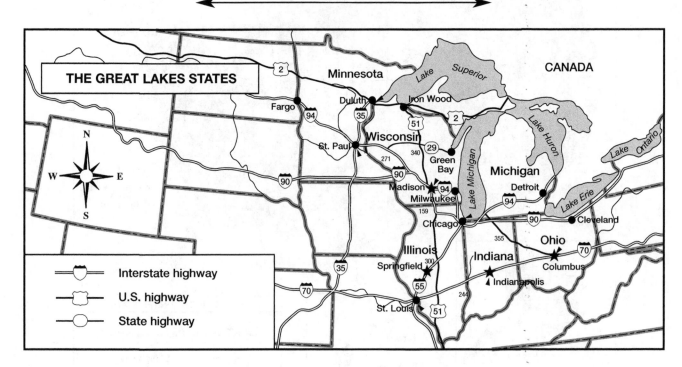

1. Read the map title. This map shows _____.

2. Read the legend. The three types of highways shown are _____,

   _____, and _____.

3. Read the compass rose. Label the intermediate directions.

4. What states are included in this region? _____

   _____

5. Trace the route from Green Bay to St. Paul. Use a green pencil or marker. What highways

   would you take? _____

6. Trace the route from Green Bay to Duluth via Iron Wood. Use a red pencil or marker. What

   highways would you take? _____

7. Where would you see this sign?

Duluth	340
St. Paul	271
Chicago	159

_____

Maps: Read, Understand, Apply 5–6, SV9781419099434

Name _____ Date _____

Finding Distance on a Route Map

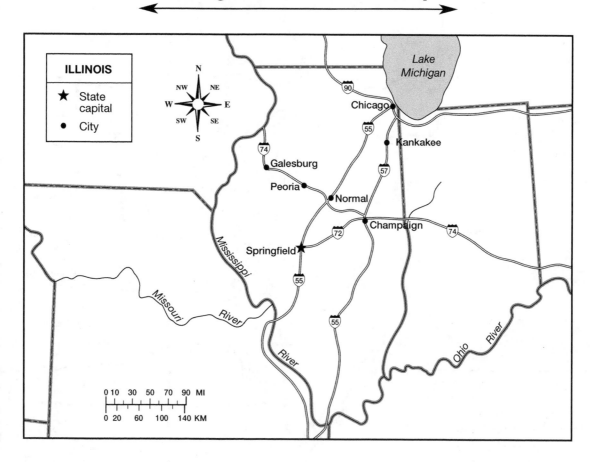

1. Circle the capital of Illinois on the map. Write its name. _____

2. Chicago is the largest city in Illinois. Find it on the map and circle it.

3. From Chicago to Springfield is about _____ miles.

4. You want to find the shortest route from Chicago to Springfield.

   a. Would you drive Interstate 57 and Interstate 72 or Interstate 55 through Normal?

   _____

   b. What direction would you be traveling? _____

5. a. From Kankakee to Champaign is about _____ miles.

   b. What direction is Champaign from Kankakee? _____

6. a. From Springfield to Champaign is about _____ miles.

   b. What direction is Champaign from Springfield? _____

7. If you drove 40 miles an hour from Springfield to Champaign, how many hours would it take?

   _____

Name _____ Date _____

Reading a Route Map of the Mountain States

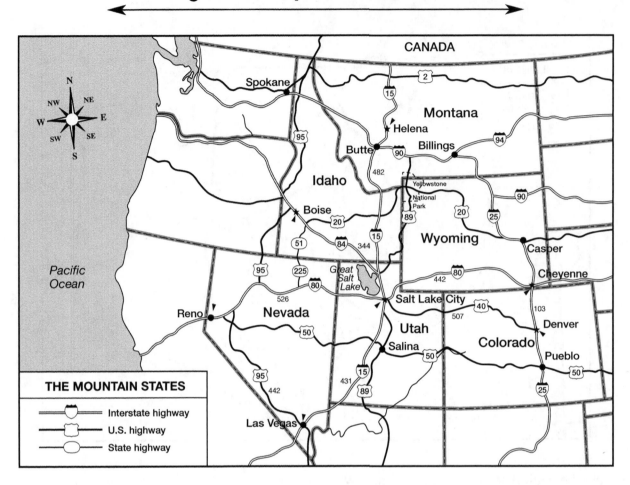

1. What region is shown here? _____

2. What states are in this region? _____

3. **a.** Trace the route from Helena to Salt Lake City in green.

   b. What highway takes you from Helena to Salt Lake City? _____

   c. How many miles is it from Helena to Salt Lake City? _____

   d. What states do you cross? _____

4. **a.** Trace the route from Helena to Cheyenne in orange. Be sure to go through Yellowstone National Park.

   b. What highways would you take? _____

5. What U.S. highway connects Interstate 84 with Interstate 80? _____

6. Where would you see this sign? (*I* stands for "Interstate.")

   ```
   ┌─────────────┐
   │  U.S. 95 ↑  │
   │  ← I-15 →   │
   └─────────────┘
   ```
   _____

Maps: Read, Understand, Apply 5–6, SV9781419099434

Name _____   Date _____

Using a Route Map

←————————————————→

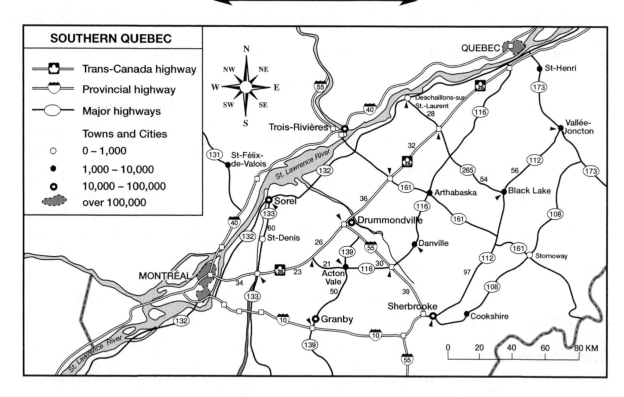

1. What highway takes you from Granby to Acton Vale? _____

2. a. How many kilometers is it from Acton Vale to the interchange just south of Granby?

   (Read the mileage marker.) _____

   b. Use the map scale to measure the distance "as the crow flies" (in a straight line) from Acton

   Vale to the interchange just south of Granby. The distance is about _____ kilometers.

   c. Why do you think the distances differ? _____

   _____

3. a. What is the distance "as the crow flies" from the interchange on Highway 55 southeast of

   Drummondville to Granby? _____

   b. What is the distance along the highways? _____

4. a. Where is the junction of Highways 112 and 265? _____

   b. If you drove 54 kilometers northwest of that junction, what junction would you come to?

   _____

5. a. What highway goes along the southern shore of the St. Lawrence River? _____

   b. Where would you exit that highway to get to Black Lake? _____

Practice Your Skills

Write the word or phrase from the box that best completes the sentence.

1. An _____ crosses the entire country.

2. A _____ crosses several states.

3. To find distances on route maps, use the

_____.

4. A _____ crosses one state.

5. An area with many things in common is a _____.

6. An _____ is a junction of major highways and has special connecting ramps or roads.

Vocabulary Practice

route   interstate highway
U.S. highway   state highway
scenic road   region
mileage markers
junction   interchange

Map Skills Practice

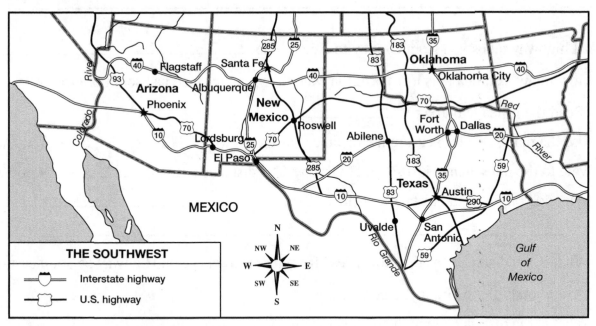

7. What interstate highway splits to go through Dallas and Fort Worth? _____

8. What route goes through the capital of Arizona? _____

9. What route goes along part of the Red River? _____

10. What interstate highways would you take from Flagstaff to Abilene via Albuquerque and

El Paso? _____

48

Drawing a Region of the United States

Select a region of the United States. Use the space below to draw a map of the region you have selected and label the major transportation centers (railroad, airports, and seaports) and routes (highways, railroads, and inland waterways). Your map should include a title, compass rose, legend, and map scale (if possible).

Name _____ Date _____

✦ Geography Theme: Human/Environment Interaction

Human/Environment Interaction describes how people change or adapt to the environment. Some changes to the land cause problems. In North Africa, much of the land is desert. In what ways would a desert environment affect the people who live there? In some areas of North Africa, **desertification** has become a problem. Desertification is the spread of desert conditions into the neighboring environment. This results in an increase in the size of the desert.

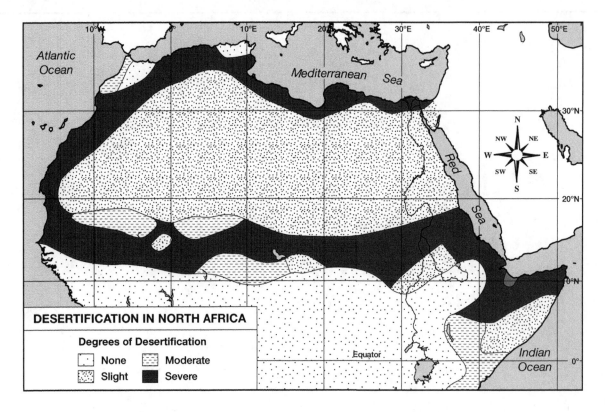

DESERTIFICATION IN NORTH AFRICA

Degrees of Desertification
- None
- Slight
- Moderate
- Severe

1. How much desertification is shown along the Mediterranean Sea? _____

_____

2. Describe the degrees of desertification along the equator.

_____

_____

3. Explain why it would be helpful for geographers to know the locations, kinds, and causes of desertification in North Africa.

_____

_____

Name _____ Date _____

For hundreds of years, the Dutch people of the Netherlands have worked to **reclaim,** or take back, land that has been flooded. They built dikes around the flooded areas and drained the water. The Dutch call this reclaimed land "polders."

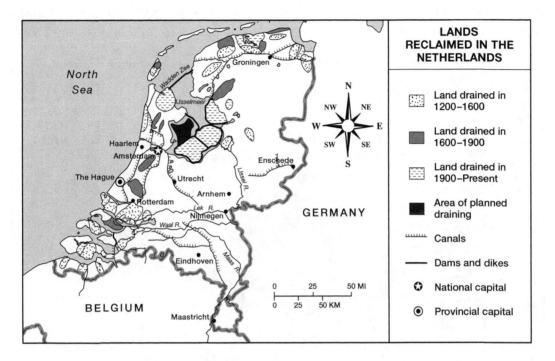

1. During which time period did the Dutch reclaim the most land? _____

_____

2. Along which bodies of water was land reclaimed? _____

_____

3. What is the location of future polders? _____

_____

4. Based on the map, how have the Dutch worked with their environment besides building polders,

   dams, and dikes? _____

_____

5. How would you describe the interaction of the Dutch with their environment? How has it been

   helpful or harmful? Explain. _____

_____

Name _____ Date _____

Sometimes people create problems in the environment. An example is pollution. One kind of pollution is **acid rain**—pollution that mixes with water vapor and falls to the ground in the form of rain or snow. This pollution comes from factories, power plants, and cars and trucks that burn coal, oil, and gas. Acid rain kills fish and destroys forests. It pollutes drinking water and soil and damages buildings. The map below shows recent acid rain levels in the United States and Canada.

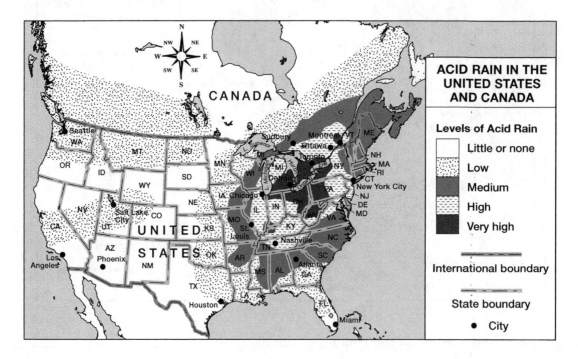

1. According to the map, where are the highest levels of acid rain found? _____

_____

_____

_____

2. Describe acid rain levels in western Canada and the western United States. _____

_____

3. Based on the map, where do you think most manufacturing centers are located in the United States and Canada? Explain your answer.

_____

_____

_____

Name _____ Date _____

Human/Environment Interaction includes how people depend on the environment. The map shown here demonstrates how people in Mexico use the land and its resources to meet their needs and wants.

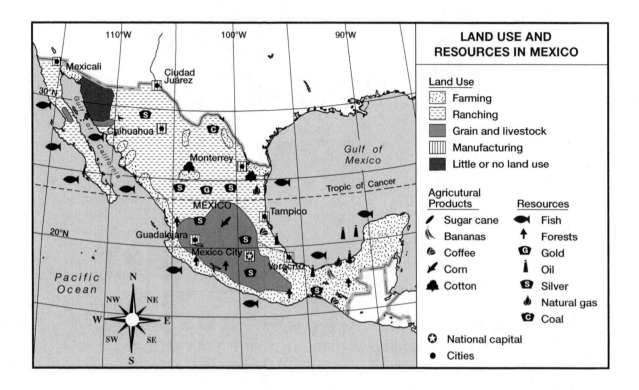

1. According to the map, where is fishing an important activity? _____

_____

_____

2. Based on the map key and map, where would you expect Mexico's population to be the smallest?

_____

3. Along which of these coasts would be a better location for oil refineries: Pacific Ocean, Gulf

of Mexico, or Gulf of California? Explain. _____

_____

_____

Name _____ Date _____

Special Purpose Maps

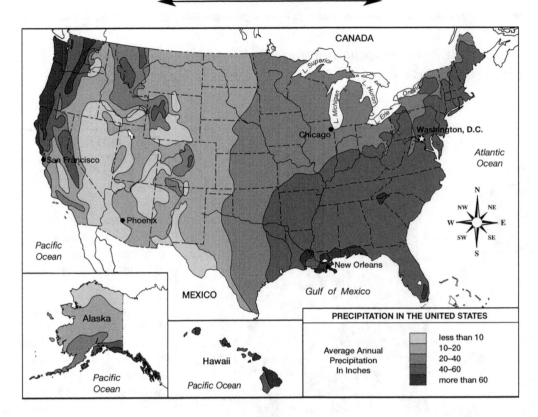

All maps have a purpose. Route maps show ways to get from one place to another. Relief maps show us how the land looks. **Special purpose maps** show information not found on other maps. The information may be about the climate, the people, the resources, or the history of an area. You need to read each map's title and legend carefully.

Use the map reading skills you've learned to read a special purpose map. Read the title carefully. The title tells you what the map shows. This map shows precipitation in the United States. Precipitation is rain and snow.

Read the legend carefully. The legend tells you what the symbols mean. On this map, shadings are used as symbols. Remember that a **symbol** is something that stands for something else. Here each shade stands for a different amount of precipitation.

1. What areas on the map get 20–40 inches of precipitation per year? _____

_____

2. Does more precipitation fall along the coastlines or inland? _____

3. Does more precipitation fall along the northwestern Pacific Coast or the northeastern Atlantic

Coast? _____

4. Which areas of the United States get the most precipitation? _____

_____

Name _____ Date _____

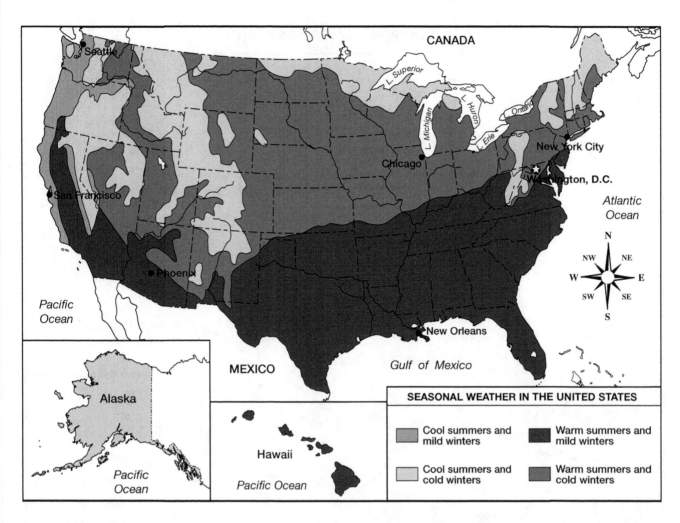

There are many types of special purpose maps. A **resource map** uses symbols for things in nature that people can use. In the legend you may find symbols for things like gold, oil, or coal. These symbols will appear on the map in the area where the resource is found.

Population maps show the number of people living in an area. The population of an area may be shown by using patterns, colors, or both.

Above is a **seasonal weather map.** It tells you what the summers and winters are like in certain parts of the country.

1. What kind of weather does New York City have? _____

2. Look at the inset map of Alaska. What kind of weather does Alaska have? _____

_____

3. What kind of weather does Seattle have? _____

4. Locate your state on the map on page 54 and the map above. Describe the climate where you live. What kind of weather and how much precipitation does your state have?

_____

Name _____ Date _____

Reading a Population Map

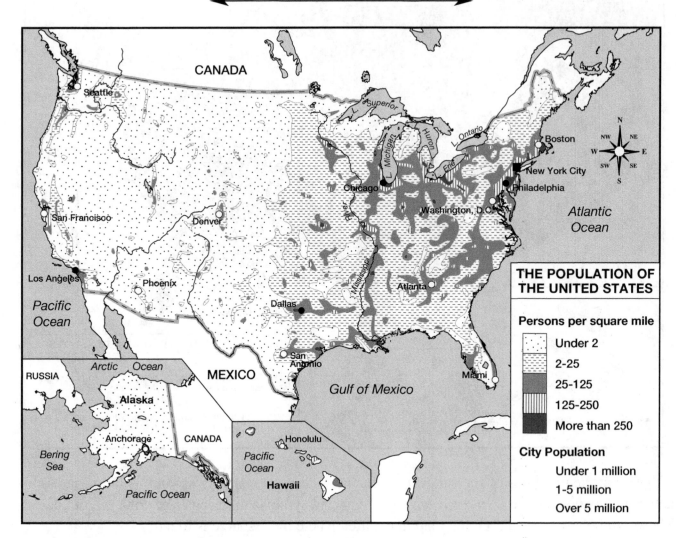

1. The purpose of this map is to show _____.

2. Add these symbols to the legend.
   ○ Under 1 million
   ● 1–5 million
   ■ Over 5 million

3. Name three cities that have 1 to 5 million people. _____,

   _____, and _____

4. What city has the largest population? _____

5. What is the average population of Alaska? _____

6. Does the eastern or western United States have the higher population? _____

Reading a Population Map
Maps: Read, Understand, Apply 5–6, SV9781419099434

Name _____ Date _____

Reading a Historical Map

←————————————→

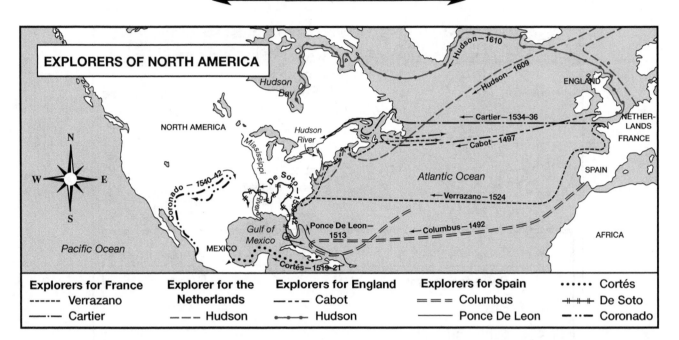

1. Read the title. This map shows _____ .

2. Read the compass rose. Label the intermediate direction arrows.

3. Find Columbus in the legend. What pattern shows his voyage? Draw it here.

_____

4. In what country did Columbus start? _____

5. **a.** Which explorer made two trips to the New World? _____

   b. Where did he begin his first voyage? _____

   c. In what years were his voyages? _____

   d. What is a body of water named after this explorer? _____

6. Trace DeSoto's route in red. What river did he cross? _____

7. Trace Coronado's route in blue. In what country did he start? _____

8. DeSoto and Coronado were explorers for what country? _____

9. Draw a conclusion. Did most of the explorers for Spain travel to the northern or southern

   regions of North America? _____

Name _____   Date _____

Reading a Movement Map

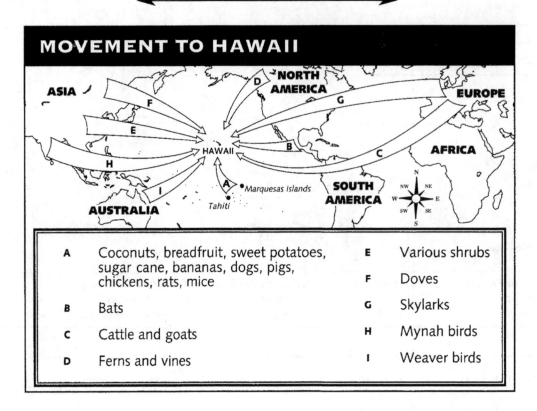

The map above shows the parts of the world that provided many new foods and animals to the islands of Hawaii. Many were brought to Hawaii by early explorers and settlers. Use the map to answer the questions.

1. Skylarks came to Hawaii from which continent? _____

2. What is the letter of the arrow that stands for *Weaver birds?* _____

3. Which animal traveled northeast from Australia to reach Hawaii? _____

4. Which plants came to Hawaii from North America? _____

5. From which continent did bats come to Hawaii? _____

Name _____ Date _____

Reading a Land Use Map

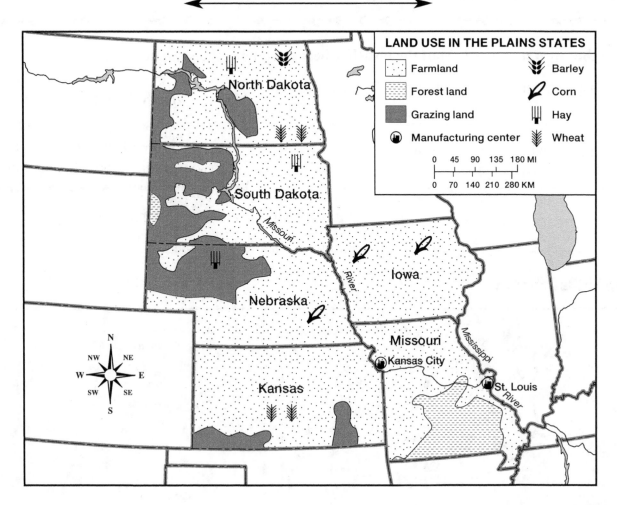

1. The purpose of this map is to show _____.

2. What is the most common use of land in these states? _____

3. In which state is barley grown? _____

4. In which states is corn grown? _____

5. What is the most common use of land in western South Dakota? _____

    _____

6. In what part of Kansas is there grazing land? _____

7. There are two manufacturing centers in this region.

    a. Circle them.

    b. What are they? _____

    c. About how far apart are they? _____

Name _____ Date _____

Practice Your Skills

Write the word or phrase from the box that best completes the sentence.

1. A map showing the number of people in an area is a

   _____.

2. A map showing special information is a

   _____.

3. A _____ shows things found in nature that people can use.

4. A _____ is something that stands for something else.

Map Skills Practice

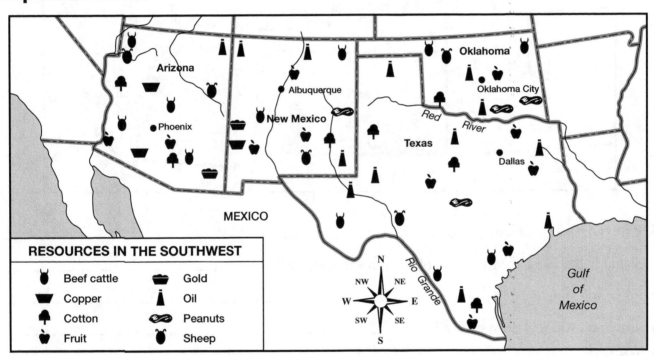

5. Gold is found in which states? _____

6. Is there more oil in Arizona or in Texas? _____

7. Cotton can be found in every state on this map. Name two other resources that can be found

   in all four states. _____ and _____

8. Which state does not grow peanuts? _____

9. Copper is found in which two states? _____

My Special Purpose Map

Select a state and create a special purpose map of that state. You may choose from a population map, historical map, movement map, weather map, or land use map. Use the space below to draw your map. Remember to include a map title, compass rose, and legend with symbols.

Name _____ Date _____

Grids

←——→

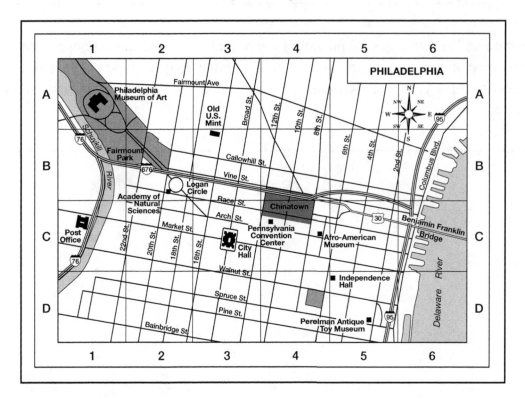

A **grid** is a pattern of lines drawn on a map to help people locate places. These lines form squares. With a grid, it is easy to find places on the map. Look at the squares on the map above. Each square in the grid is labeled with a **coordinate.** The rows of squares are labeled with a letter. The columns are labeled with a number.

Locate City Hall on the map above. It is in square C-3. Find the letter C on the left side of the map. Slide your finger across row C until you reach column 3. You are now in square C-3. Put your finger on City Hall.

1. With your finger in square C-3, move your finger one square to the east. This is square C-4.

Name two points of interest in square C-4. _____ and _____

2. Find the Perelman Antique Toy Museum. It is in square D-5. Name the historic site in this

square that you could visit. _____

3. The Philadelphia Museum of Art is in square A-1. This museum is in what park? _____

4. Put your finger on the Philadelphia Museum of Art. Slide it southeast through the park. The

park ends near Logan Circle. In what grid square is Logan Circle? _____

5. Locate the Benjamin Franklin Bridge in square C-6. What river does it cross? _____

6. What two interstate highways can be found in square B-1? _____ and _____

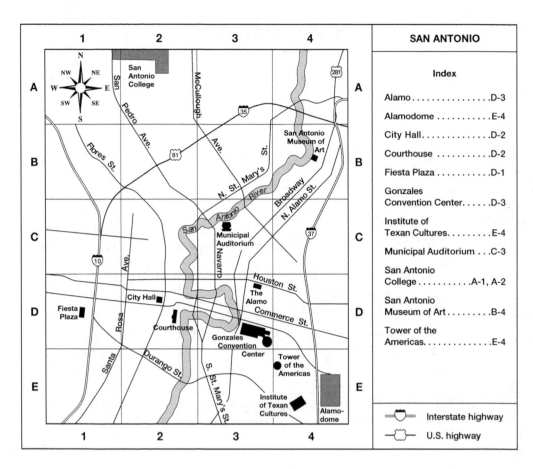

To find a place on a map grid, you can look it up in the **map index.** A map index is an alphabetical list of all the places shown on the map. A map index lists each place with its coordinate.

Look at the map above. It shows places of interest in San Antonio, Texas. To find places on the map, you use the map index. Imagine you want to visit the Alamo. Look up "Alamo" in the map index. It directs you to square D-3. Locate square D-3 on the grid. Put your finger on the Alamo.

1. Use the map index to find City Hall. In what grid square is it located? _____

2. Find City Hall on the map. Name another point of interest in this square. _____

3. Look up the San Antonio Museum of Art in the map index.

    a. In what grid square is it located? _____

    b. What direction is the San Antonio Museum of Art from City Hall? _____

4. Find San Antonio College by using the map index. In what grid squares is it located? _____

5. Locate the Institute of Texan Cultures using the map index.

    a. In what grid square is it located? _____

    b. What other point of interest is located in this same square? _____

Name _____ Date _____

Reading a Map Grid

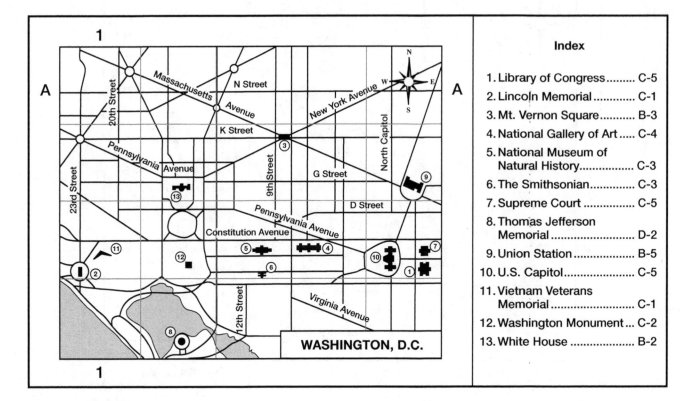

Index

WASHINGTON, D.C.

1. Read the title. This map shows _____.

2. Read the compass rose. Circle the north arrow. Label the intermediate directions.

3. Read the map grid. Add the missing letters and numbers.

4. **a.** In what square is the White House located? _____

   b. Circle it on the map.

5. **a.** In what square is the Washington Monument? _____

   b. Circle it on the map.

6. **a.** What famous memorial is south of the Washington Monument? _____

   b. What memorial is to the northwest? _____

7. **a.** In what square is the U.S. Capitol located? _____

   b. What two points of interest are to the east? _____ and _____

8. What point of interest is located in C-4? _____

Name _____ Date _____

Reading a Map Index

←——————————————→

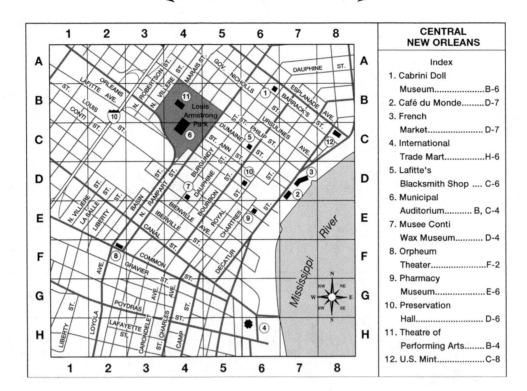

1. Find Louis Armstrong Park on the map.

   a. What two buildings are located in this park? _____

   and _____

   b. What street borders the park to the east? _____

2. Find Lafitte's Blacksmith Shop on the map.

   a. What other buildings are in that column? _____

   b. What streets border the shop on the north and east sides? _____

   and _____

3. Use the map index and grid to find the coordinates for these places on the map. Circle them in red and write the coordinates below.

   a. Café du Monde _____   **c.** Orpheum Theater _____

   b. Preservation Hall _____

4. What places could you visit if you walked southwest on Decatur from the U.S. Mint?

   _____

5. What street would you use to get from Musee Conti Wax Museum to the Orpheum Theater?

   _____

Name _____ Date _____

Using a Map Grid

←——————→

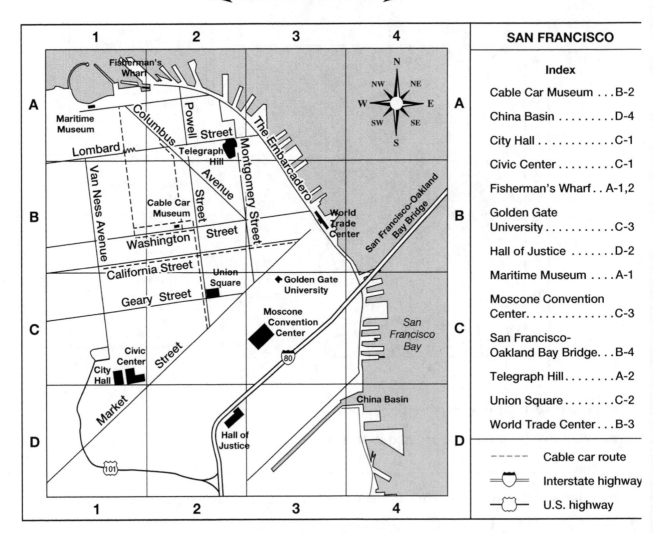

SAN FRANCISCO

Index

Cable Car Museum . . . B-2

China Basin D-4

City Hall C-1

Civic Center C-1

Fisherman's Wharf . . A-1,2

Golden Gate
University C-3

Hall of Justice D-2

Maritime Museum A-1

Moscone Convention
Center. C-3

San Francisco-
Oakland Bay Bridge. . . B-4

Telegraph Hill A-2

Union Square C-2

World Trade Center . . . B-3

- - - - - Cable car route

⬡═══ Interstate highway

⬡—— U.S. highway

1. **a.** In what grid square do you find the Maritime Museum? _____

   b. Circle it in red on the map.

2. **a.** In what grid square is the Cable Car Museum located? _____

   b. Circle it blue on the map.

3. What direction is the Maritime Museum from the Cable Car Museum? _____

4. Trace the cable car route from the Cable Car Museum to Union Square. Is Union Square

   east or west of the cable car route? _____

5. What interstate highway is in San Francisco? _____

6. What U.S. highway is in San Francisco? _____

Name _____ Date _____

Using a Map Grid of New York City

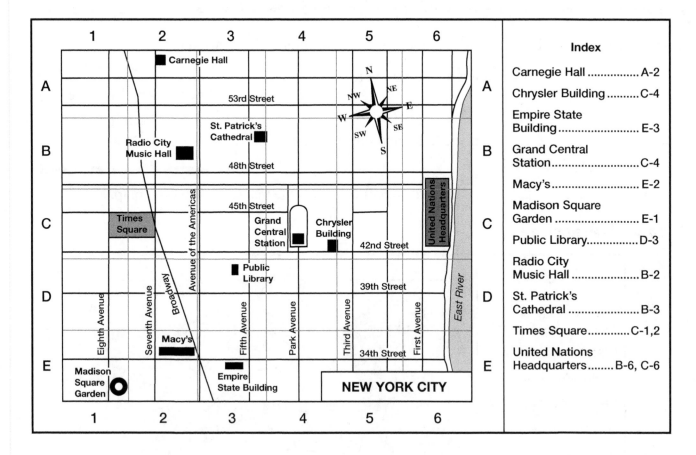

1. **a.** In what squares is the United Nations Headquarters located? _____

   b. What avenue goes along the west side of the United Nations Headquarters? _____

2. **a.** In what grid squares is Times Square located? _____

   b. Draw a line along 42nd Street from the United Nations Headquarters to Times Square.

   c. Name one building you would pass on this route. _____

3. **a.** In what grid square is Radio City Music Hall located? _____

   b. Draw your route from Times Square to Radio City Music Hall in blue.

   c. What avenue is just east of Radio City Music Hall? _____

4. **a.** In what grid square is the Empire State Building? _____

   b. Draw your route from Radio City Music Hall east to Fifth Avenue in red.

   c. Draw your route to the Empire State Building in green.

   d. What street is just north of the Empire State Building? _____

Name _____   Date _____

Practice Your Skills

Write the word or phrase from the box that best completes the sentence.

1. A pattern of lines drawn on a map is called a

   _____.

2. A _____ is the letter and number that
   identifies a grid square.

3. A _____ is an alphabetical list of all the places shown on a map.

Map Skills Practice

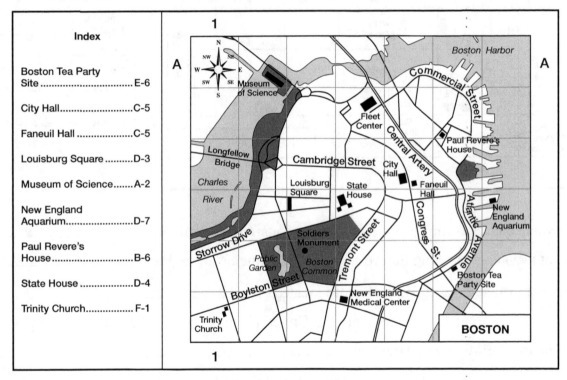

4. Complete the grid by adding the missing letters and numbers.

5. In what grid square do you find City Hall? _____

6. In what grid square do you find Paul Revere's House? _____

7. What direction is Paul Revere's House from City Hall? _____

8. In what grid square is the New England Aquarium located? _____

9. What direction is the Aquarium from Paul Revere's House? _____

10. In what grid square is the Boston Tea Party Site located? _____

My Walking Tour of Washington, D.C.

Use the map on page 64 to create a walking tour of Washington, D.C. You will have limited time in the U.S. capital city, so you may select only seven points of interest. Write directions for your tour, using cardinal and intermediate directions and the points of interest you have selected. Your directions will explain how you will travel from place to place.

_____

_____

_____

_____

_____

_____

_____

_____

_____

_____

_____

_____

_____

_____

_____

_____

_____

_____

_____

_____

Geography Theme: Regions

Regions describe places that share one or more features. A region can be called physical because it is marked by a physical feature, such as climate. The Great Plains is a physical region of the United States that has grasslands as its common feature. A region can be called a human region if it is marked by a human feature, such as language.

The map shows the major urban centers in the United States and Canada. Each center is made up of several large cities and their suburbs that have increased in size and grown together. You can hardly tell where one city begins and another ends. Each urban center on the map can be considered a region.

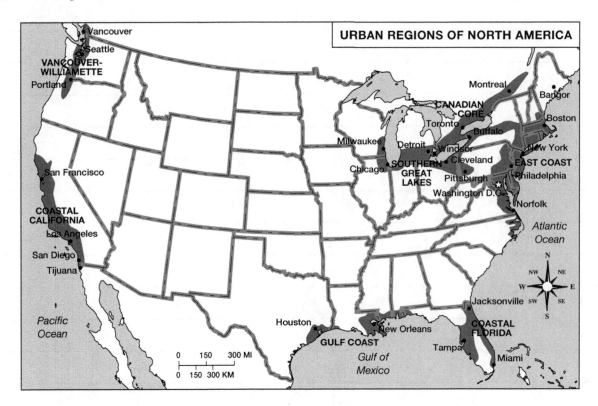

1. What is similar about the location of each urban region in North America?

_____

2. Use a ruler and the map scale. How many miles long is the Coastal California urban region?

_____

3. What cities make up the Vancouver-Willamette urban region?

_____

Name _____ Date _____

Regions can be as large as a hemisphere or as small as a neighborhood. The map shows neighborhoods in New Orleans that can be considered regions.

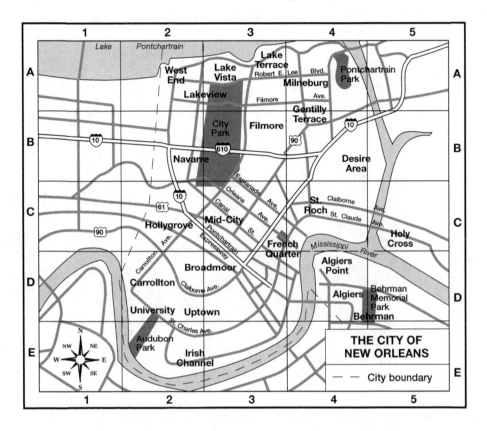

1. The Garden District is found in grid square D-3. This region has many old mansions and beautiful gardens. Label the *Garden District* on the map.

2. What feature do you think is common to the neighborhood of Lakeview according to this map?

_____

3. What special features would you expect to find in the French Quarter?

_____

_____

4. How could these neighborhood regions help the government of New Orleans organize the city?

_____

_____

_____

Name _____   Date _____

Regions are places that are similar in one or more ways. Geographers categorize areas into regions based on one feature, such as the climate or type of government. They also recognize regions by a number of features, such as landforms, soil, language, history, and climate.

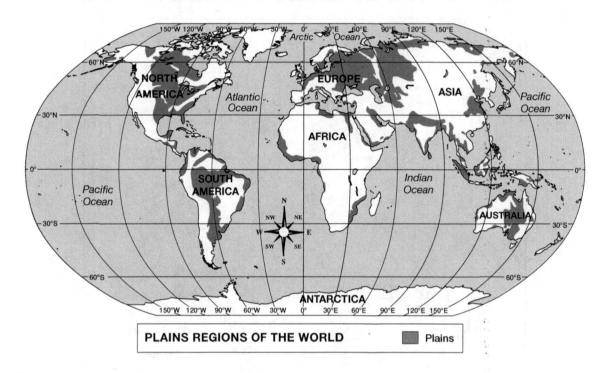

PLAINS REGIONS OF THE WORLD   ▨ Plains

1. What kind of feature—physical or human—describes this region?

_____

2. Which continent has no plains?

_____

3. In what part of South America are plains mostly located?

_____

4. In what two ways might plains regions differ from mountain regions of the world?

_____

_____

_____

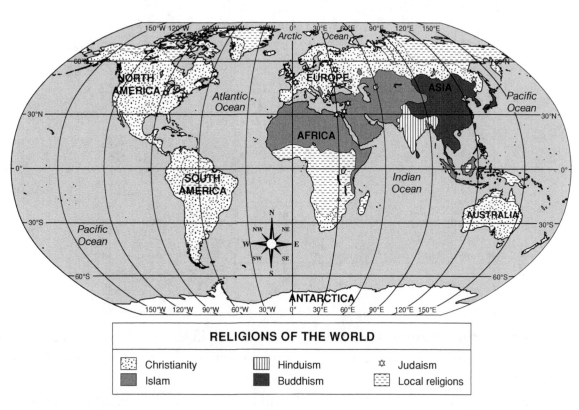

RELIGIONS OF THE WORLD

░ Christianity	▥ Hinduism	✡ Judaism
▓ Islam	▨ Buddhism	░ Local religions

1. What kind of feature—physical or human—describes the regions on this map?

_____

2. What is the major religion of North America?

_____

3. In what part of the world is Buddhism a major religion?

_____

4. In what parts of the world is Judaism practiced?

_____

5. Why might knowing the major religion of a region help you understand more about the region?

_____

_____

Name _____ Date _____

Latitude and Longitude

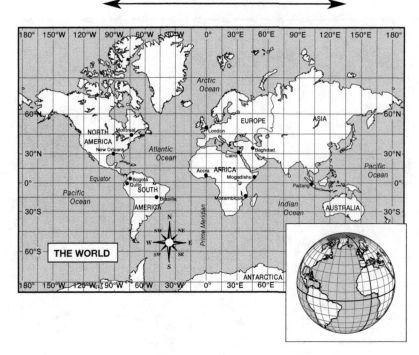

Many maps have grids and grid coordinates to help locate places. World maps and globes have grids on them. Look at the world map above. The grid pattern on the map is made up of lines of **latitude** and of **longitude.**

The lines that go east and west are the lines of latitude. They are also called **parallels** because they never touch each other. Latitude is used to measure distances north and south of the Equator. The Equator is 0° latitude. The symbol ° stands for **degrees.**

The lines that go north and south are the lines of longitude. They are also called **meridians.** Longitude is used to measure distances east and west of the **Prime Meridian.** The Prime Meridian is 0° longitude and goes from the North Pole to the South Pole. All lines of longitude meet at the North and South Poles.

1. Find the Equator on the map above. What cities lie near the Equator? _____

_____

2. Look north of the Equator to find 30° North latitude. What cities lie near this line of latitude?

_____

3. Find 15° South latitude. What cities lie near this line of latitude? _____

_____

4. Find the Prime Meridian. What cities lie near the Prime Meridian? _____

5. Look east of the Prime Meridian to find 45° East longitude. What cities lie near this line

of longitude? _____

6. Find 75° West longitude. What cities lie near this line of longitude? _____

Maps: Read, Understand, Apply 5–6, SV9781419099434

Name _____   Date _____

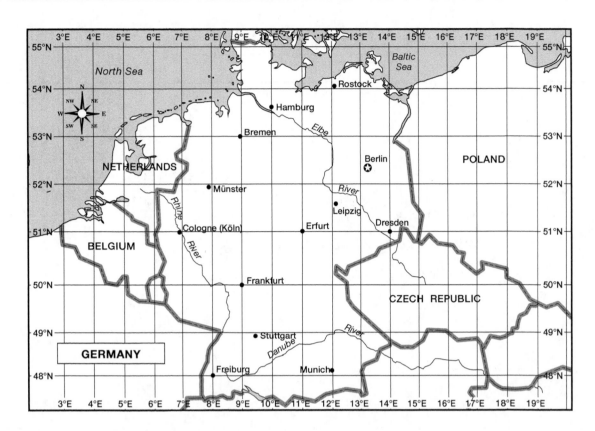

Look at the map of the world on page 74. You can see that the lines of latitude begin with 0° at the Equator and increase as they go north and south. The highest numbers are at the poles. The North Pole is 90° North latitude, and the South Pole is 90° South latitude.

The lines of longitude begin with 0° at the Prime Meridian and increase as they go east and west of the Prime Meridian. The highest number is 180°. The line of longitude directly opposite the Prime Meridian is 180°.

The lines of latitude and longitude form a grid pattern. This grid enables us to locate every place on Earth. Look at the map above. Find 51° North latitude. Run your finger along it until it crosses 7° East longitude. You have found the city of Cologne. The coordinates of Cologne are 51° North latitude and 7° East longitude, or 51°N, 7°E. Every spot on Earth has its own coordinates.

1. Use latitude and longitude coordinates to find these places on the map. The coordinate for latitude is always named first. Circle each place as you find it.

   a. Frankfurt 50°N, 9°E

   b. Bremen 53°N, 9°E

   c. Munich 48°N, 12°E

2. Estimate the coordinates (latitude and longitude) of these places on the map.

   a. Münster _____

   b. Leipzig _____

   c. Stuttgart _____

Finding Longitude

←——————————→

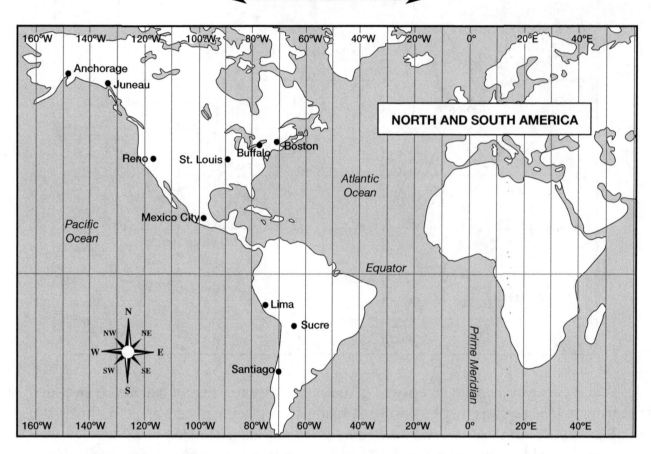

1. Are North and South America east or west of the Prime Meridian? _____

2. North and South America are in which hemisphere? _____

3. **a.** Trace the 150°W meridian in green.

   b. What city is near 150°W? _____

4. **a.** Trace the 120°W meridian in red.

   b. What city is near 120°W? _____

5. **a** Trace the 80°W meridian in orange.

   b. What city is nearest 80°W? _____

6. **a.** Find Lima in South America. Circle it.

   b. Estimate the longitude of Lima. _____

7. **a.** Find Sucre in South America. Circle it.

   b. Estimate the longitude of Sucre. _____

8. What city is north of the Equator and near 70°W longitude? _____

76

Name _____ Date _____

Finding Latitude

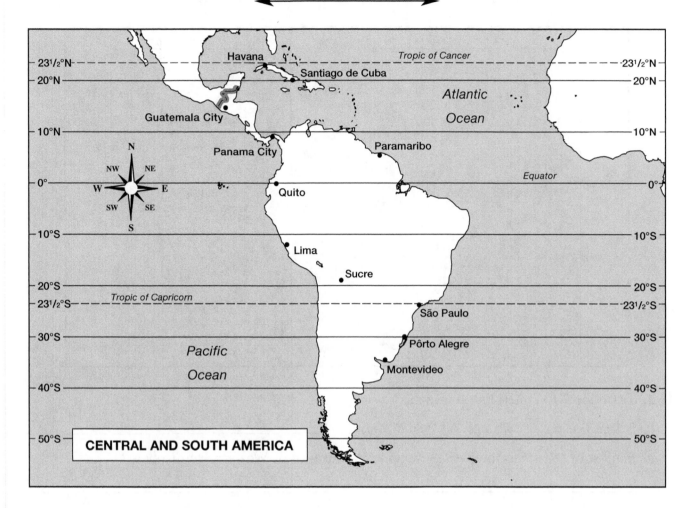

CENTRAL AND SOUTH AMERICA

1. What city lies on the Equator? _____

2. What city lies near the Tropic of Cancer? _____

3. What city lies near the Tropic of Capricorn? _____

4. What city lies near 20°N? _____

5. What city lies near 10°N? _____

6. Guatemala City lies between 20°N and 10°N. Estimate its latitude. _____

7. Paramaribo lies between 10°N and the Equator. Estimate its latitude. _____

8. Montevideo lies between 30°S and 40°S. Estimate its latitude. _____

9. What city lies near 30°S? _____

10. Lima lies between 10°S and 20°S. Estimate its latitude. _____

Name _____   Date _____

Finding Latitude and Longitude

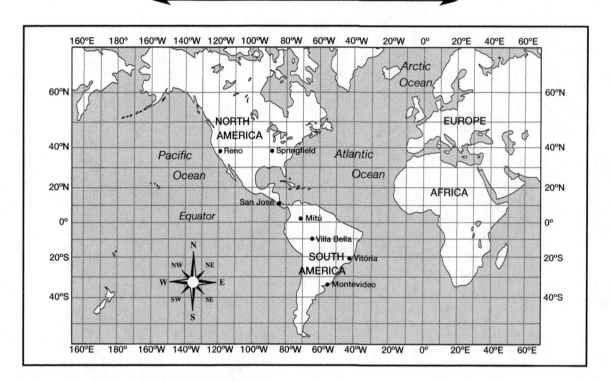

1. **a.** Trace the 70°W meridian in green.

   b. Is that line east or west of the Prime Meridian? _____

   c. Is most of the area shown on the map in the Eastern or Western Hemisphere?

   _____

2. **a.** Trace the Equator in red.

   b. Draw an **N** just north of the Equator.

   c. Draw an **S** just south of the Equator.

3. **a.** What city is near the place where the Equator and 70°W cross? _____

   b. What are its coordinates? _____, 70°W

4. Find the missing coordinate for these cities.

   a. Springfield 40°N, _____

   b. Vitória _____, 40°W

   c. Reno _____, 120°W

   d. San José 10°N, _____

   e. Villa Bella _____, 65°W

   f. Montevideo 35°S, _____

Using Latitude and Longitude

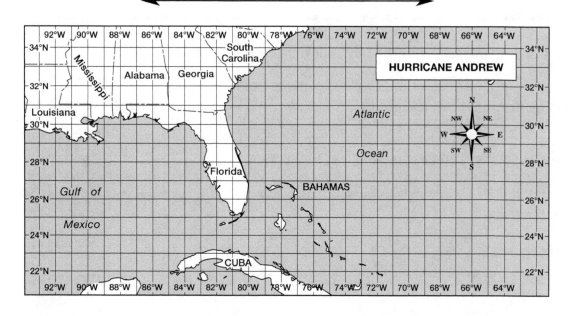

1. Use the latitude and longitude coordinates to track Hurricane Andrew's path on the map above. Put a dot on the map for each coordinate. Number each dot. Connect the dots to track Hurricane Andrew's path.

Position	Latitude	Longitude	Position	Latitude	Longitude
1	24°N	63°W	9	26°N	85°W
2	25°N	65°W	10	$26\frac{1}{2}$°N	87°W
3	26°N	69°W	11	$27\frac{1}{2}$°N	89°W
4	$25\frac{1}{2}$°N	72°W	12	29°N	91°W
5	$25\frac{1}{2}$°N	74°W	13	30°N	$91\frac{1}{2}$°W
6	$25\frac{1}{2}$°N	$76\frac{1}{2}$°W	14	31°N	$91\frac{1}{2}$°W
7	$25\frac{1}{2}$°N	79°W	15	$31\frac{1}{2}$°N	91°N
8	$25\frac{1}{2}$°N	81°W	16	32°N	90°W

2. Write the direction that Hurricane Andrew traveled

   a. from Position 1 to Position 3. _____

   b. from Position 4 to Position 8. _____

   c. from Position 9 to Position 13. _____

   d. from Position 14 to Position 16. _____

3. In what body of water did the hurricane begin? _____

4. What other body of water did it cross? _____

5. Where did Hurricane Andrew hit land? _____

Maps: Read, Understand, Apply 5–6, SV9781419099434

Name _____ Date _____

Practice Your Skills

Write the word or phrase from the box that best completes the sentence.

1. The _____ is the starting point for measuring distances east and west.

2. Lines of latitude, also called _____, measure distances north and south of the Equator.

3. Line of longitude, also called _____, meet at the poles.

Vocabulary Practice

latitude meridians degrees
parallels longitude
Prime Meridian

Map Skills Practice

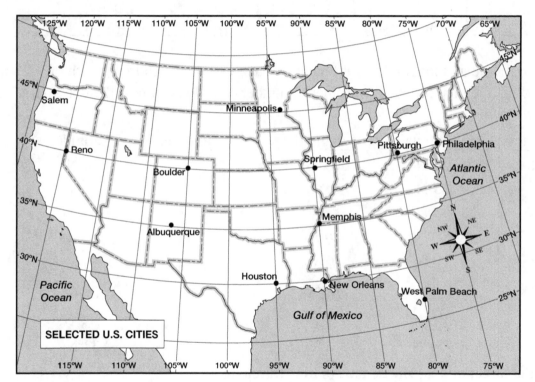

SELECTED U.S. CITIES

4. List the cities at these locations.

   a. 40°N, 90°W _____ **c.** 40°N, 105°W _____

   b. 40°N, 75°W _____ **d.** 35°N, 90°W _____

5. Write the latitude and longitude coordinates of these cities.

	Latitude	Longitude		Latitude	Longitude
a. New Orleans	_____	_____	**c.** Reno	_____	_____
b. Pittsburgh	_____	_____	**d.** Houston	_____	_____

Locating Coordinates

Use the world map on page 106 to determine the location of several rivers and mountains around the world. Use the space below to create lists of rivers and mountains and their coordinates. An example has been given.

River	Coordinates
Mississippi	40°N, 90°W

Mountain	Coordinates

Maps: Read, Understand, Apply 5–6, SV9781419099434

Name _____   Date _____

Climate Maps

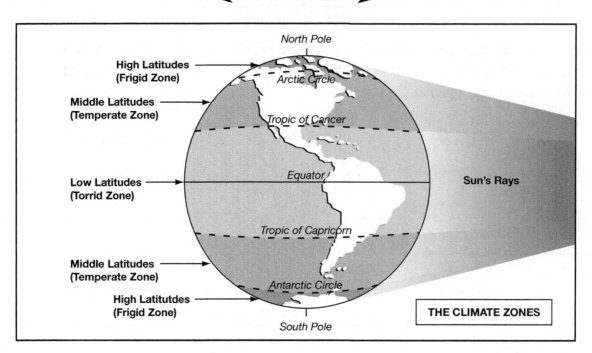

THE CLIMATE ZONES

Climate is the weather of an area over a long period of time. Many different factors determine what kind of climate a place has. Some factors include elevation, winds, and whether the place is near water.

One of the most important factors in determining climate is how directly the rays of the sun hit the place. Because Earth is round, the sun's rays do not hit it evenly. In places near the Equator, the sun is directly overhead. These places receive direct rays. In places near the poles, the sun is low in the sky. These places receive slanted rays. The direct rays give more heat. The slanted rays give less heat.

The world can be divided into **climate zones** based on how directly the sun's rays strike Earth. Look at the map above to find the climate zones.

The **low latitudes,** or **Torrid Zone,** are between the Tropic of Cancer ($23\frac{1}{2}°$N) and the Tropic of Capricorn ($23\frac{1}{2}°$S). *Torrid* means "very hot." The sun's direct rays heat the Torrid Zone all year around.

The **high latitudes,** or **Frigid Zones,** cover the area between the Arctic Circle ($66\frac{1}{2}°$N) and the North Pole (90°N) and the area between the Antarctic Circle ($66\frac{1}{2}°$S) and the South Pole (90°S). *Frigid* means "very cold." The sun is low in the sky in these areas, so only slanted rays hit them. As a result, these zones are cold all year.

The **middle latitudes,** or **Temperate Zones,** are between the Torrid Zone and the Frigid Zones. *Temperate* means "balanced." The climate in the Temperate Zones is a balance between the heat of the Torrid Zone and the cold of the Frigid Zones. The climate of places in the Temperate Zones changes from season to season.

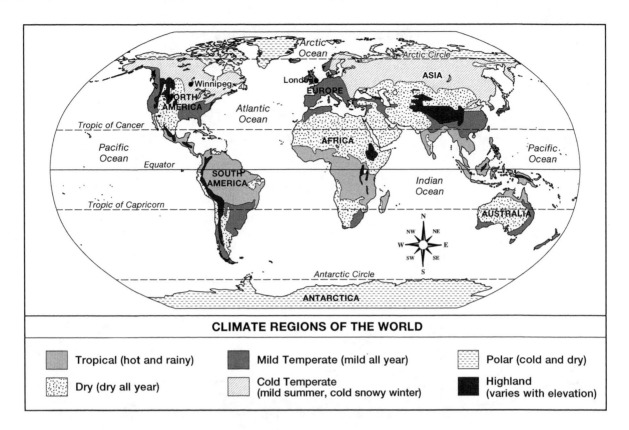

CLIMATE REGIONS OF THE WORLD

Tropical (hot and rainy)	Mild Temperate (mild all year)	Polar (cold and dry)
Dry (dry all year)	Cold Temperate (mild summer, cold snowy winter)	Highland (varies with elevation)

Not all places within a climate zone have the same climate. For example, Winnipeg, Canada, and London, England, are both in the Temperate Zone. The rays of sunlight that strike Winnipeg are about as direct as the ones that strike London. Yet the two places have very different climates. London has a much warmer climate because it is near the sea. This is an example of how factors other than sunlight affect the climate of a place.

To reflect differences within climate zones, a list of **climate regions** has been developed. There are six basic types of climate found on Earth. As you read about the climate regions of the world, locate them on the map above.

The **tropical climate** is hot and rainy. Many of the world's rain forests and jungles grow in tropical climates.

Areas that have a **dry climate** are dry all year round. Much of the western United States has a dry climate. So does northern Africa, where the great Sahara desert is.

The **mild temperate climate** is mild all year.

Areas with **cold temperate climates** have mild summers, but the winters are cold and snowy.

Areas with a **polar climate** are cold and dry.

Mountainous areas have a **highland climate,** which varies with the elevations.

1. Find the polar climates on the map. Why do you think this climate has the name it does?

_____

2. Every place on Earth has one of these six climate regions. Find where you live on the map.

In which climate region do you live? _____

Name _____ Date _____

Mastering Climate Zones

⟵⟶

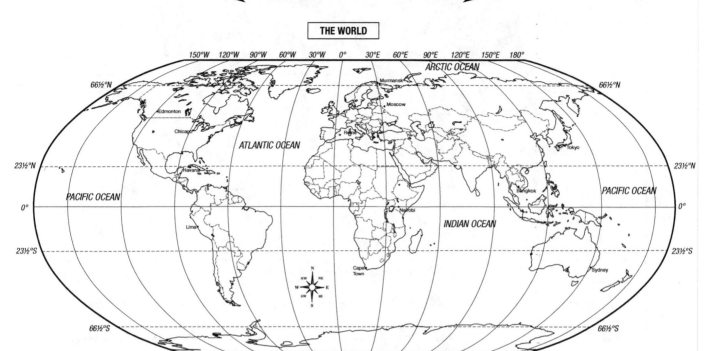

1. Label the following places on the map. Write two labels twice.

Equator	Tropic of Cancer
Arctic Circle	Frigid Zone
Antarctic Circle	Tropic of Capricorn
Torrid Zone	Temperate Zone

2. Lightly color the Torrid Zone orange, the Temperate Zones yellow, and the Frigid Zones blue.

3. After each city below, write its climate zone. Then write whether it is in the high, middle, or low latitudes.

Place	Climate Zone	Latitudes
a. Murmansk	_____	_____
b. Chicago	_____	_____
c. Cape Town	_____	_____
d. Nairobi	_____	_____
e. Tokyo	_____	_____
f. Havana	_____	_____
g. Rome	_____	_____
h. Bangkok	_____	_____
i. Lima	_____	_____

➤➤➤➤➤➤➤➤➤➤➤➤➤➤➤➤➤➤➤➤➤➤➤➤➤➤

Maps: Read, Understand, Apply 5–6, SV9781419099434

Name _____ Date _____

Reading a Climate Map of Turkey

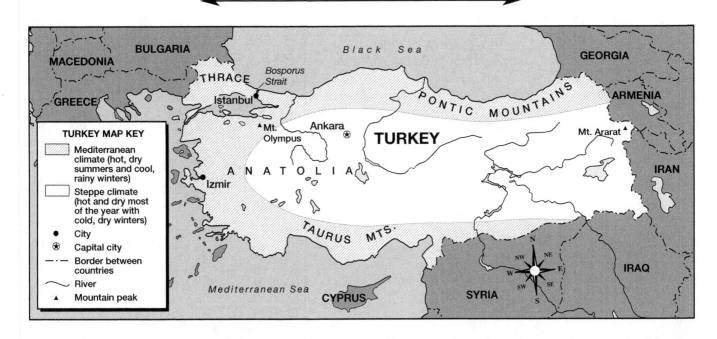

1. What is the national capital of Turkey? _____

2. What kind of climate does the land along Turkey's two coasts have? _____

3. What kind of climate is common around Mt. Ararat? _____

4. What kind of winters does Ankara have? _____

5. What kind of summers does Izmir have? _____

6. What kind of climate do the mountainous regions have? _____

7. Compare the winters of Mt. Ararat to the winters of Mt. Olympus.

_____

_____

_____

8. Describe the climate along Turkey's eastern border.

_____

_____

_____

Name _____ Date _____

Reading a Climate Map

←—————————————————→

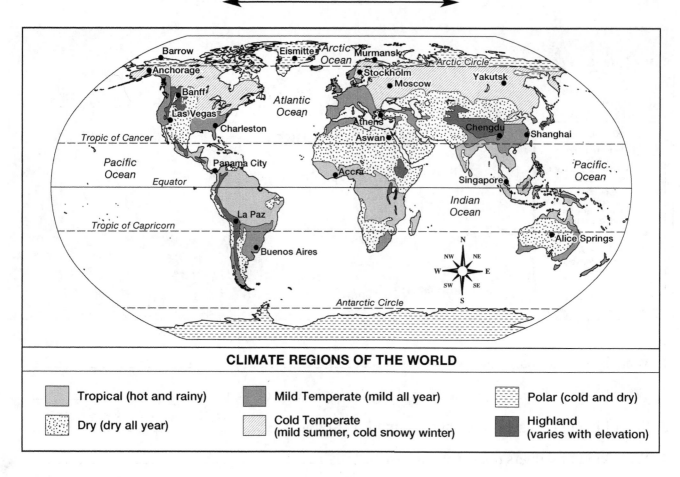

CLIMATE REGIONS OF THE WORLD

▨ Tropical (hot and rainy)	▨ Mild Temperate (mild all year)	▨ Polar (cold and dry)
▨ Dry (dry all year)	▨ Cold Temperate (mild summer, cold snowy winter)	▨ Highland (varies with elevation)

This map shows six climate regions of the world.

1. Write the name of three cities in each climate region.

a. Tropical _____ _____ _____

b. Dry _____ _____ _____

c. Mild Temperate _____ _____ _____

d. Cold Temperate _____ _____ _____

e. Polar _____ _____ _____

f. Highland _____ _____ _____

2. Which climate is found mostly in the Frigid Zone? _____

3. The tropical region is found mostly in what climate zone? _____

4. Draw a conclusion. Which has the most areas with cold snowy winters, the Northern or

the Southern Hemisphere? _____

Name _____ Date _____

Reading a Climate Map of Europe

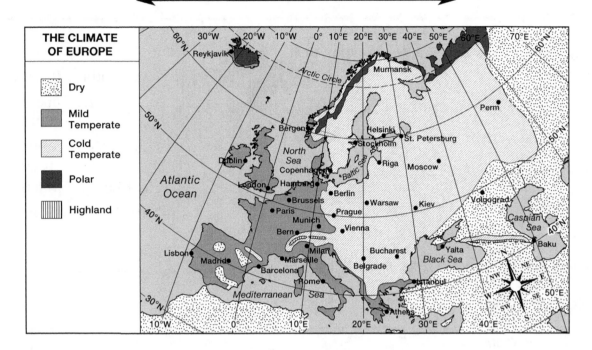

1. This map shows _____.

2. What type of climate does most of Europe have? _____

3. List the cities at these locations. Then write the climate region.

   a. 60°N, 25°E   _____   _____

   b. 50°N, 45°E   _____   _____

   c. 60°N, 5°E   _____   _____

   d. 45°N, 20°E   _____   _____

   e. 55°N, 5°W   _____   _____

4. Estimate the degrees latitude and longitude of each city. Then write its climate region.

	Latitude	Longitude	Climate Region
a. St. Petersburg	_____	_____	_____
b. Kiev	_____	_____	_____
c. London	_____	_____	_____
d. Baku	_____	_____	_____
e. Madrid	_____	_____	_____

5. Polar regions on this map do not extend below what line of latitude? _____

Practice Your Skills

Write the word or phrase from the box that best completes the sentence.

Vocabulary Practice

Torrid Zone
high latitudes   climate
Temperate Zone
middle latitudes
Frigid Zone   low latitudes

1. The Temperate Zone is found in the _____.

2. The area between the Tropic of Cancer and the Tropic of

   Capricorn is called the _____,

   or the _____.

3. The high latitudes are also called the _____.

4. The weather of an area over a long period of time is its _____.

Map Skills Practice

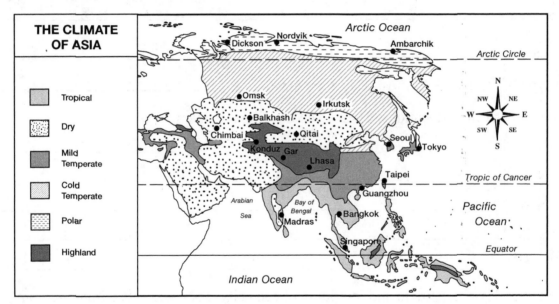

5. Write the names of three cities in each climate region.

   a. Tropical _____ _____ _____

   b. Dry _____ _____ _____

   c. Mild Temperate _____ _____ _____

   d. Cold Temperate _____ _____ _____

   e. Polar _____ _____ _____

   f. Highland _____ _____ _____

Making a Diagram of Seasons

Use an encyclopedia or the Internet, along with the information from pages 82 and 83, to create a diagram explaining why it is summer in the Southern Hemisphere when it is winter in the Northern Hemisphere. Use the space below to draw your diagram. Remember to label all parts of your diagram.

Maps: Read, Understand, Apply 5–6, SV9781419099434

Name _____ Date _____

Time Zones

←————————→

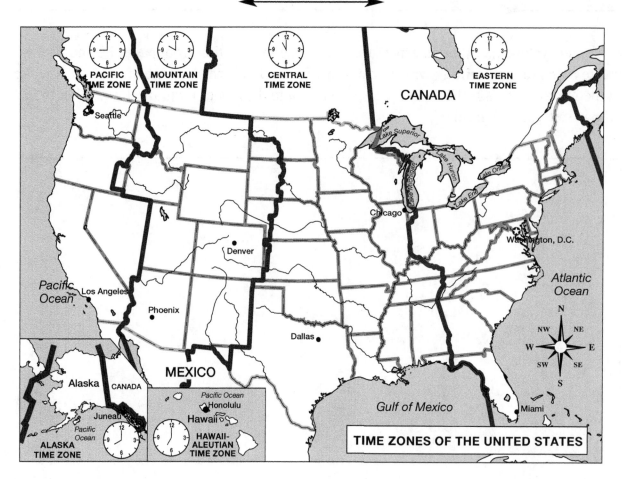

TIME ZONES OF THE UNITED STATES

You know that Earth is turning all the time. It makes one complete rotation, or turn, every 24 hours. Remember that Earth gets its light from the sun. Only half of Earth receives light at a time. As Earth turns, one part it gets lighter while another part gets darker.

It is not the same time everywhere on Earth. Earth is divided into 24 **standard time zones.** There is one time zone for each hour in the day.

Six of the world's 24 time zones are in the United States. Look at the time zone map above. The time in each zone is different by one hour from the zone next to it. Washington, D.C., is in the Eastern Time Zone. Chicago is in the Central Time Zone. When it is 8:00 A.M. in Washington, D.C., it is 7:00 A.M. in Chicago. In Denver, which is in the Mountain Time Zone, it is 6:00 A.M. In San Francisco, which is in the Pacific Time Zone, it is 5:00 A.M. In the Alaska Time Zone, it is 4:00 A.M. In the Hawaii-Aleutian Time Zone, it is 3:00 A.M.

1. In which time zone do you live? _____

2. How do you think the Pacific Time Zone got its name? _____

3. What mountain range goes through the Mountain Time Zone? _____

4. New York City is in which time zone? _____

Maps: Read, Understand, Apply 5–6, SV9781419099434

Name _____   Date _____

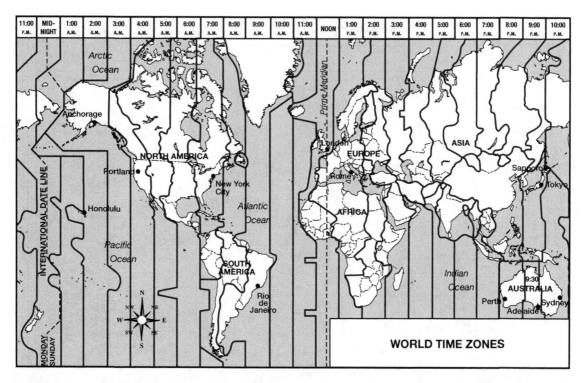

Look at the time zone map above. The time in each zone is different by one hour from the zone next to it. Earth rotates toward the east. So as you travel west, the time is one hour earlier every time you cross into a new time zone. As you travel east, the time is one hour later.

Find London on the Prime Meridian (0 degrees). It is in the time zone labeled *NOON*. Now find Rome. It is one time zone east of London, so the time is one hour later. When it is 12:00 noon in London, it is 1:00 P.M. in Rome. Now find Rio de Janeiro. It is three time zones west of London, so the time is three hours earlier. When it is 12:00 noon in London, it is 9:00 A.M. in Rio de Janeiro.

Find the **International Date Line** on the map above. This imaginary line, at about 180° longitude, separates one day from the next. The time of day is the same on both sides of the line. But west of the line, it is one day later than it is to the east. If it is midnight Sunday on the east side of the line, it is midnight Monday on the west side of the line.

Notice that the time zones often follow political boundaries. This keeps places in one state, country, or area all in the same time zone. Some places around the world do not observe standard time zones and use different times. Find central Australia on the map. Notice that in Adelaide it is 9:30 when it is 8:00 in Perth.

1. How many time zones is New York City from London? _____

2. Which direction is New York City from London? _____

3. What time is it in New York City when it is 12:00 noon in London? _____

4. How many time zones is Honolulu from Rio de Janeiro? _____

5. Which direction is Honolulu from Rio de Janeiro? _____

6. What time is it in Honolulu when it is 6:00 P.M. in Rio de Janeiro? _____

Name _____ Date _____

Reading a Time Zone Map

TIME ZONES OF THE UNITED STATES

1. Lightly color the time zones. Use a different color for each zone. Notice that the lines are not always straight. Time zones often follow state boundaries or physical features.

2. In which time zone do you find these states?

   a. California _____   **c.** Pennsylvania _____

   b. Illinois _____   **d.** Hawaii _____

3. It is 10:00 A.M. in California. What time is it in Wyoming? _____

4. It is 5:00 P.M. in Georgia. What time is it in Alaska? _____

5. It is 12:00 noon in Illinois. What time is it in Virginia? _____

6. It is 4:00 P.M. in Massachusetts. What time is it in Oklahoma? _____

7. It is 12:00 midnight in Iowa. What time is it in New Mexico? _____

8. It is 4:30 A.M. in Colorado. What time is it in Washington state? _____

Name _____ Date _____

Using a Time Zone Map

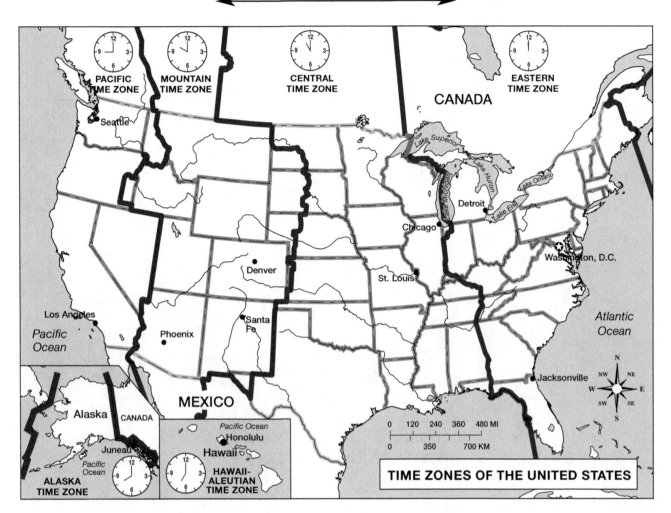

1. You will be traveling to several cities in the United States. Draw a line from Jacksonville to

   St. Louis. What direction will you be traveling? _____

2. When you arrive in St. Louis, it is 2:00 P.M. What time is it in Jacksonville? _____

3. From St. Louis, you will drive to Denver. Draw a line to connect these two cities.

4. From St. Louis to Denver is about _____ miles.

5. What direction will you be traveling? _____

6. You will drive from Denver to Los Angeles to visit friends. Draw a line connecting these
   two cities.

7. It is 7:00 A.M. in Los Angeles. What time is it in Denver? _____

8. What time is it in Jacksonville? _____

Name _____ Date _____

Understanding World Time Zones

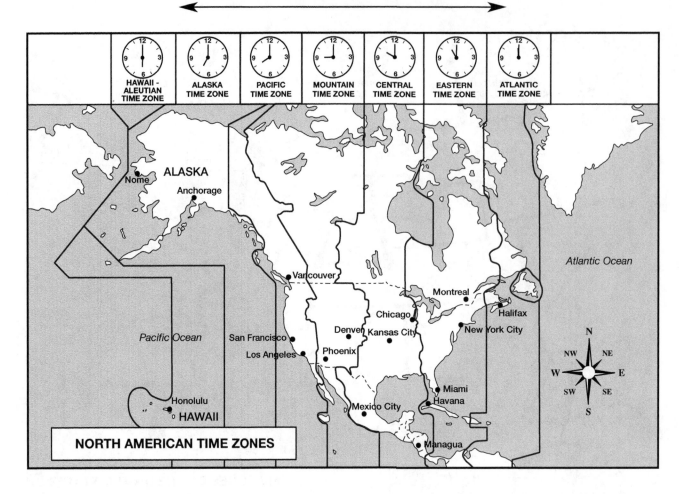

1. Lightly color each time zone a different color. Follow the lines along state boundaries or physical features.

2. It is 12:00 noon in the Atlantic Time Zone. Write the correct times on the clocks for the other time zones. Remember, the time is one hour earlier as you travel west.

3. If it is 8:00 A.M. in Los Angeles, what time is it in each city listed below?

   a. Vancouver _____   **e.** Miami _____

   b. Kansas City _____   **f.** Denver _____

   c. Honolulu _____   **g.** New York City _____

   d. Anchorage _____   **h.** Halifax _____

4. The World Series is at 6:00 P.M. in New York City. What time is it in each city listed below?

   a. Montreal _____   **d.** Phoenix _____

   b. Mexico City _____   **e.** San Francisco _____

   c. Nome _____   **f.** Honolulu _____

Name _____ Date _____

Mastering World Time Zones

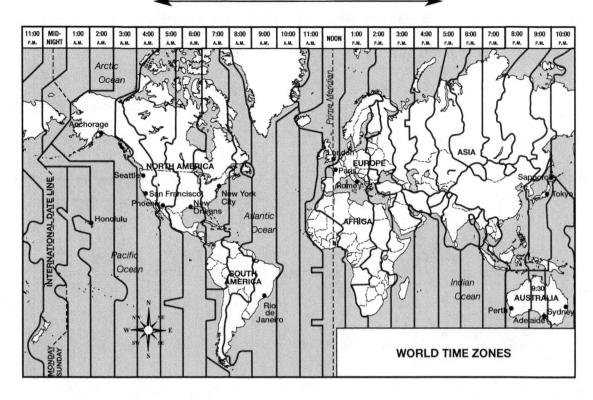

1. If it is 12:01 P.M. Tuesday in London, what time and day is it halfway around the world?

_____

2. How many time zones does each of these continents have?

  a. Africa _____   **b.** South America _____

3. If you go from Tokyo to Sydney, how many time zones do you cross? _____

4. If you go from Seattle to Rio de Janeiro, how many time zones do you cross? _____

5. If you go from Honolulu to New Orleans, how many time zones do you cross? _____

6. It is 7:00 A.M. in Phoenix. What time is it in Paris? _____

7. It is 3:00 A.M. in Rio de Janeiro. What time is it in San Francisco? _____

8. Suppose you fly from Anchorage to New York City. Do you set your watch ahead or back?

  By how many hours? _____

9. You travel from London to Tokyo. Do you set your watch ahead or back? By how many hours?

_____

Maps: Read, Understand, Apply 5–6, SV9781419099434

Name _____ Date _____

Practice Your Skills

Write the phrase from the box that best completes the sentence.

1. Earth has 24 _____.

2. When you go west across the _____,
it is suddenly tomorrow and you lose a day.

Map Skills Practice

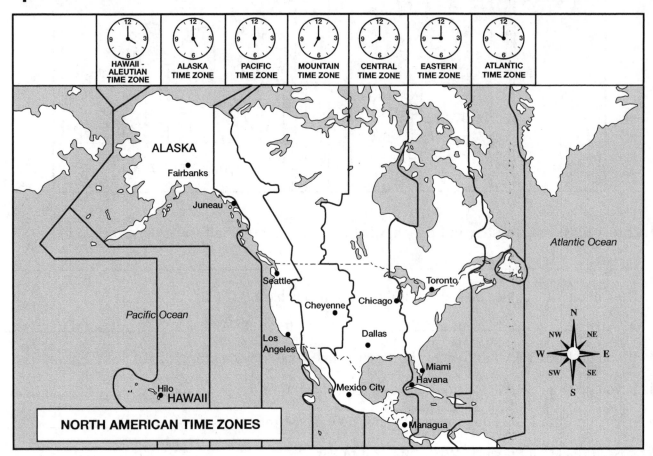

NORTH AMERICAN TIME ZONES

3. Dallas is in the _____ Time Zone.

4. Seattle is in the _____ Time Zone.

5. Toronto is in the _____ Time Zone.

6. The president gave a speech at 9:00 P.M. Eastern Time. What time was it in these cities?

    a. Los Angeles _____

    b. Chicago _____

    c. Hilo _____

    d. Havana _____

    e. Cheyenne _____

    f. Juneau _____

Name _____ Date _____

Managing My Business

Imagine that you are the owner of a business in Hawaii. You must make frequent phone calls and plane trips to Sydney, Australia. Use the phone log below to record the time when phone calls are made in Hawaii and when they are received in Sydney.

Phone Log

Made in Hawaii	Received in Sydney
_____	_____
_____	_____
_____	_____
_____	_____
_____	_____
_____	_____
_____	_____

Use the space below to create an itinerary for a business trip you are taking from Hawaii to Sydney. List the time and day of your departure from Hawaii and the time and day of your arrival in Sydney. Remember to consider the International Date Line. Then list the time and day of your departure from Sydney and the time and day of your arrival in Hawaii.

Itinerary from Hawaii to Sydney

Depart Hawaii   **Arrive Sydney**

_____   _____

Itinerary from Sydney to Hawaii

Depart Sydney   **Arrive Hawaii**

_____   _____

Maps: Read, Understand, Apply 5–6, SV9781419099434

Geography Theme: Location

Location tells where something is found. Every place on Earth has a location. There are two ways of naming a location. **Relative location** tells what it is near or what is around it. **Absolute location** gives the exact location by using latitude and longitude.

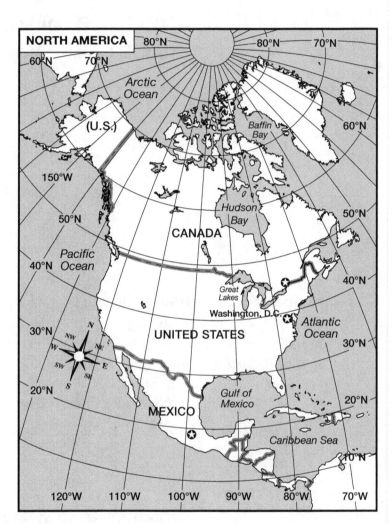

1. Greenland, the largest island in the world, is located northeast of Canada and east of Baffin Bay. Most of Greenland is north of the Arctic Circle. Label *Greenland* on the map.

2. Label the following national capitals on the map.

   a. Mexico City 19°N, 99°W

   b. Ottawa 45°N, 76°W

3. Label the following on the map.

   a. Mt. McKinley 63°N, 151°W

   b. Grand Canyon 36°N, 112°W

   c. Lake Superior 48°N, 89°W

4. Find Mexico on the map. Describe the relative location of Mexico.

   _____

   _____

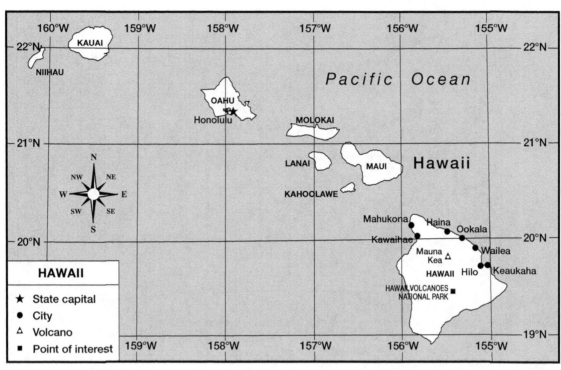

1. Describe the relative location of Honolulu. Explain why its location might be one reason Honolulu was chosen as the capital of Hawaii.

_____

_____

_____

2. Estimate the absolute location of the volcano Mauna Kea—the highest point in Hawaii.

_____

3. Where are most cities and towns on the island of Hawaii located? Why do you think this is so?

_____

_____

_____

_____

Name _____ Date _____

Caribbean Sea

80°W 70°W 60°W 50°W 40°W

10°N

Caracas

Georgetown
Paramaribo
GUYANA   Cayenne
SURINAME
FRENCH
GUIANA

Bogotá

COLOMBIA

Atlantic
Ocean

Quito
ECUADOR

0°

Amazon   River

PERU

B R A Z I L

10°S

MATO GROSSO
PLATEAU   B R A Z I L I A N

Brasília

Sucre   HIGHLANDS

20°S

PARAGUAY

Pacific
Ocean   Asunción

CHILE

30°S

Mount Aconcagua   URUGUAY   Atlantic
Ocean   N
Santiago   NW   NE
Buenos   W   E
Aires   Montevideo   SW   SE
S

ARGENTINA

40°S

SOUTH AMERICA

50°S
International boundary
Capital City

Use the map on page 100 to answer the questions.

1. Venezuela is in the northern part of South America. This country is located along the Caribbean Sea. Label *Venezuela* on the map.

2. This South American country is found in the central part of the continent. It is southeast of Peru and north of Argentina. Write the name of the country here and then label it on the map.

   _____

3. Label these national capitals on the map.

   a. Lima 12°S, 77°W

   b. Cayenne 5°N, 52°W

4. Mount Aconcagua's absolute location is 33°S, 70°W. Circle Mount Aconcagua on the map.

5. Name the cities found at these locations.

   a. 5°N, 75°W _____   **c.** 26°S, 58°W _____

   b. 19°S, 65°W _____   **d.** 6°N, 55°W _____

6. Find the Amazon River. Describe its relative location.

   _____

   _____

   _____

7. What is the absolute location of the Mato Grosso Plateau? _____

   _____

8. Name the country located at 33°S, 55°W. _____

9. Give the absolute location of Brasília, Brazil. _____

10. Describe the relative location of the country of Guyana.

    _____

    _____

    _____

Name _____ Date _____

Final Assessment

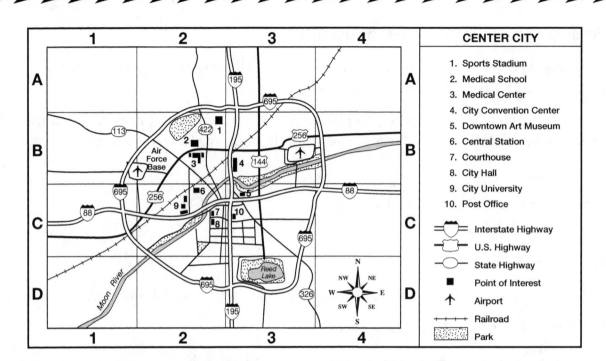

Use the city map to answer the questions. Circle the correct answers.

1. In what grid square is the airport located?

    a. A-3   **b.** C-2   **c.** B-3   **d.** D-3

2. Which two highways meet in the center of the city?

    a. 256 and 88   **b.** 422 and 113   **c.** 195 and 88   **d.** 195 and 695

3. Which human feature is located in C-2?

    a. 195   **c.** The air force base

    b. The park along the river   **d.** The river

4. Which two buildings are located in grid square C-2?

    a. Courthouse and City Hall   **c.** City Convention Center and Central Station

    b. Courthouse and Post Office   **d.** Downtown Art Museum and Central Station

Use the city map to answer the questions.

5. Suppose you want to go from the east side to the west side of the city. What highway should you take to avoid traffic in town? _____

6. Which route should you take to get from downtown to the airport? _____

Name _____ Date _____

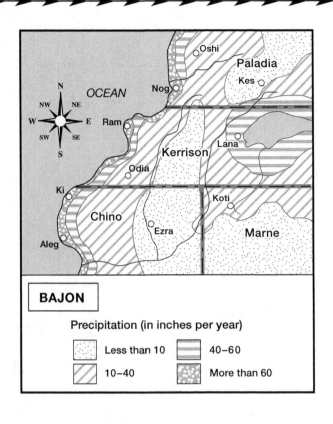

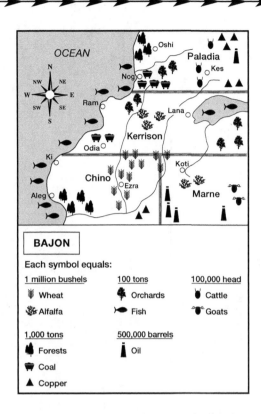

The maps above show four states of the imaginary country Bajon. Use the maps to answer the questions. Circle the correct answers.

7. Which of the following cities receives the least amount of precipitation every year?
   a. Oshi
   b. Ram
   c. Aleg
   d. Ezra

8. What is the primary agricultural product grown in the state of Chino?
   a. Alfalfa
   b. Wheat
   c. Orchards
   d. Cattle

9. In which of the following cities is coal the most important resource?
   a. Nog
   b. Oshi
   c. Koti
   d. Kes

10. How much of Bajon's oil is produced in Paladia?
   a. All
   b. More than half
   c. Half
   d. Less than half

Use the maps to answer the questions.

11. About how many tons of fish are caught each year from the ocean? _____

12. What is the annual precipitation in southern Marne? _____

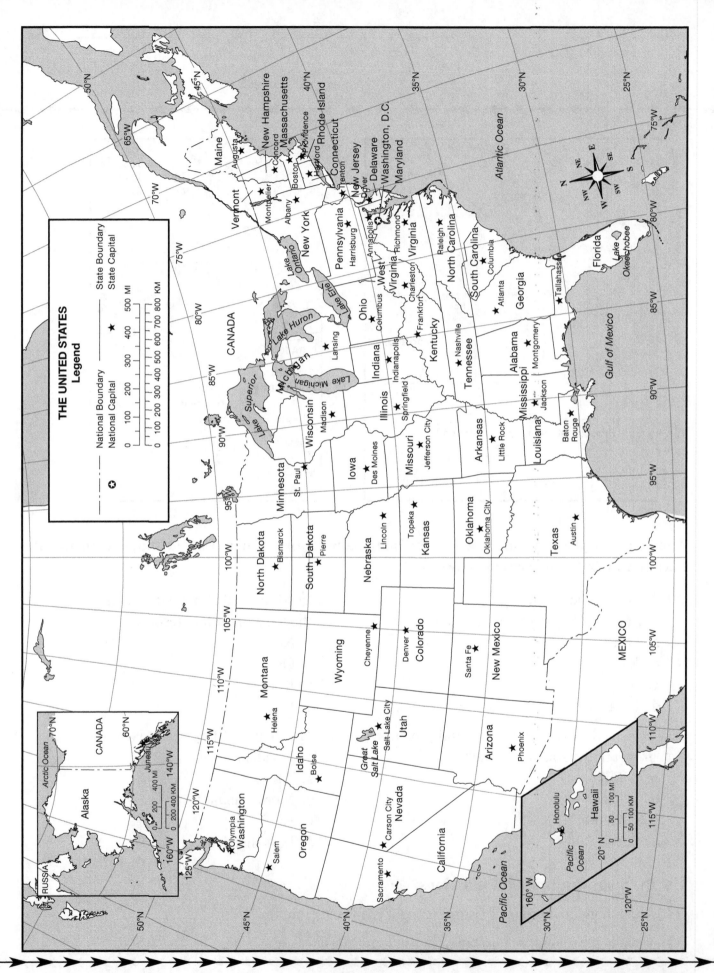

Atlas: United States
Maps: Read, Understand, Apply 5–6, SV9781419099434

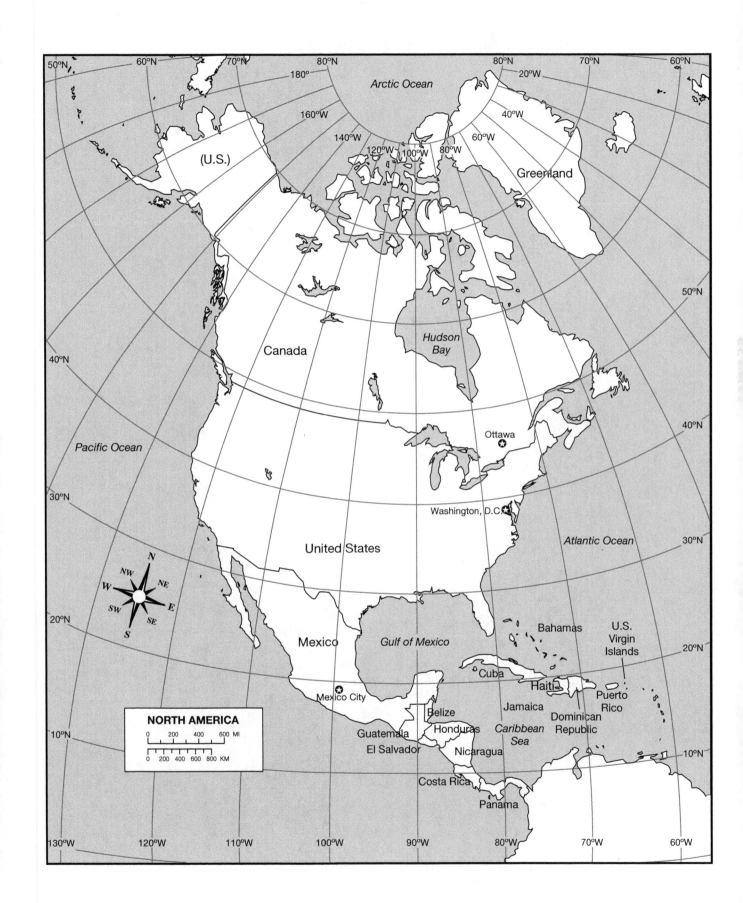

NORTH AMERICA

0   200   400   600 MI

0   200 400 600 800 KM

Atlas: North America
Maps: Read, Understand, Apply 5–6, SV9781419099434

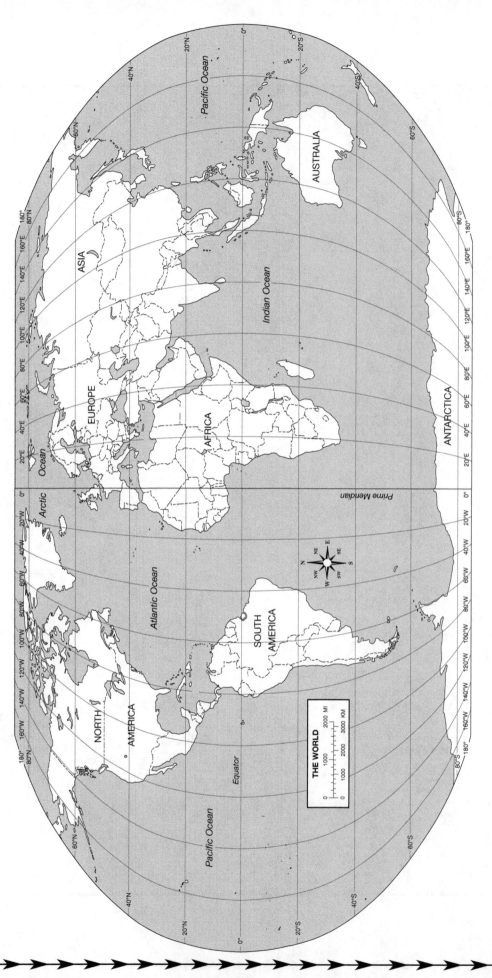

Glossary

absolute location (p. 98) the specific address or latitude and longitude coordinates of a place

acid rain (p. 52) pollution that mixes with water vapor and falls to the ground in the form of rain or snow

cardinal directions (p. 14) north, south, east, and west

climate (p. 82) the average weather of a place over a long period of time

climate region (p. 83) one of six basic types of climate found on Earth

climate zone (p. 82) an area with a generally similar climate

compass rose (p. 15) a symbol that shows the cardinal and intermediate directions: north, northeast, east, southeast, south, southwest, west, and northwest

coordinates (p. 62) the letter and number that identify a grid square; the latitude and longitude of a place

degrees (p. 74) the unit of measurement used for lines of latitude and longitude

desertification (p. 50) the spread of desert conditions to neighboring areas

direction (p. 14) notations that help compare locations

Frigid Zones (p. 82) the high latitudes that are cold all year

geography (p. 6) the study of Earth and the ways people live and work on Earth

grid (p. 62) a pattern of lines that cross each other to form squares

high latitudes (p. 82) the Frigid Zones north of the Arctic Circle and south of the Antarctic Circle that are cold all year

human/environment interaction (p. 7) the ways that the environment affects people and people affect the environment

human features (p. 6) features of a place or region made by people, such as buildings, roads, parks, playgrounds, bridges, railroads, farms, factories, and shopping malls

inset map (p. 35) a small map within a larger map

interchange (p. 42) a junction on a major highway with special connecting ramps to allow vehicles to change roads without interrupting the flow of traffic

interdependence (p. 30) how people depend on one another to meet their needs and wants

intermediate directions (p. 15) northeast, southeast, southwest, northwest

international boundary (p. 22) where one country ends and another country begins

International Date Line (p. 91) an imaginary line at about 180° longitude where the day changes

interstate highway (p.42) a main highway that crosses the entire country

junction (p. 42) a place where two highways cross or meet

kilometer (p. 34) a unit of length used in measuring distance in the metric system. A kilometer can also be written KM and km.

latitude (p. 74) the distance north or south of the Equator measured in degrees

legend (p. 22) a map key, or list of symbols on a map and what they stand for

location (p. 9) where something is found

longitude (p. 74) the distance east or west of the Prime Meridian measured in degrees

low latitudes (p. 82) the tropics, or Torrid Zone, between the Tropic of Cancer and the Tropic of Capricorn that is warm all year

map index (p. 63) the alphabetical list of places on a map with their grid coordinates

map scale (p. 34) the guide that tells what the distances on a map equal in the real world

meridians (p. 74) lines of longitude

middle latitudes (p. 82) the Temperate Zones between the high latitudes and low latitudes where weather changes from season to season

mileage markers (p. 43) small triangles and numbers on a map used to indicate distances along highways

mile (p. 34) a unit of length used in measuring distance. A mile can also be written MI or mi.

movement (p. 6) how and why people, goods, information, and ideas move from place to place

North Pole (p. 14) the point farthest north on Earth

parallels (p. 74) lines of latitude

physical features (p. 6) features of a place or region formed by nature, such as bodies of water, landforms, climate, natural resources, and plants and animals

place (p. 6) physical and human features of a location that make it different from other locations

political map (p. 23) a map that shows the boundaries separating states and countries

population map (p. 55) a map that shows how many people live in an area

Prime Meridian (p. 74) the line of longitude running from the South Pole to the North Pole and measured at 0°

reclaim (p. 51) to take back, such as land that has been flooded

regions (p. 8) areas that share one or more features

relative location (p. 98) describing a location by what it is near or what is around it

resource map (p. 55) a map that uses symbols to show things in nature that people can use, such as coal, oil, and gold

route (p. 42) a road or path from one place to another, such as a trail, highway, railroad, or waterway

scenic road (p. 42) a road that goes through beautiful areas

seasonal weather map (p. 55) a map that shows weather for an area

South Pole (p. 14) the point farthest south on Earth

special purpose map (p. 54) a map that gives information about a specific subject, such as climate, people, resources, or history

standard time zones (p. 90) Earth is divided into 24 time zones. Each time zone has a clock time one hour earlier than the zone to its east.

state boundary (p. 22) where one state ends and another begins

state highway (p. 42) a main road that connects cities and towns within the boundaries of one state

symbol (p. 22)   a picture on a map that stands for something real

Temperate Zones (p. 82) the middle latitudes where the weather changes from season to season

themes (p. 6) main topics

title (p. 23) the name of a map

Torrid Zone (p. 82) the low latitudes, or tropics, that are warm all year round

U.S. highway (p. 42) a main highway that passes through more than one state

Maps: Read, Understand, Apply 5–6, SV9781419099434

Answer Key

Pages 6–9
1. Answers will vary.
2. Answers may include: railways, highways, rivers, airplanes, pipelines, Internet, radio, television, ships, trucks, telephones
3. Information/Ideas
4. People/Goods
5. In cold weather, people wear heavy, warm clothing to keep them warm. In warm or hot weather, people wear lighter-weight clothing to keep them cool.
6. Irrigation provides the water necessary to grow crops when there is little rain.
7. Corn Belt States: Iowa, Illinois, Nebraska, Minnesota, Indiana, Ohio, Wisconsin, Missouri, Michigan, South Dakota. The Corn Belt is a region defined by common land use—the growing of corn.
8. Answers will vary.
9. Answers will vary.
10. This home is located by a lake near a hill and woods.

Page 10
1. Ensure that Big Cypress Swamp is labeled.
2. Answers may include any three of the following: The Everglades, Suwannee River, lakes, bays, Florida Keys
3. Ensure that John F. Kennedy Space Center is labeled and noted with an **H.**

Page 11
1. Physical features: Kanda River, Sumida River; Human features: parks, gardens, government buildings, shrines, stock exchange, temples, museums, banks, universities, roads, and theaters
2. Answers may include: Imperial Palace, National Diet Building, foreign embassies, national library
3. Answers will vary.

Page 12
1. Answers may include: dam, bridge, power plant, road
2. Answers may include: river, riverbank, clouds
3. Human features allow people to capitalize on physical features.

Page 13
1. Ensure the Ottawa River is correctly labeled with a **P** next to it.
2. Answers may include any two of the following: Rideau River, Rideau Falls, Dow's Lake, Ottawa River
3. Answers may include any four of the following: Supreme Court, Parliament Building, National Library, railroad station, Prime Minister's house, City Hall, University of Ottawa, Museum of Science and Technology, Ottawa International Airport, roads
4. Answers will vary.

Page 14
1. south
2. north
3. west
4. east

Page 15
1. NW   2. SW   3. SE

Page 16
1. Ensure the compass rose is correctly labeled.
2. **a.** Nebraska   **c.** Missouri
   b. Oklahoma   **d.** Colorado
3. Wyoming
4. Mississippi
5. Missouri
6. South Dakota
7. the Pacific Ocean
8. the Gulf of Mexico

Page 17
1. Ensure the compass rose is correctly labeled.
2. **a.** north   **d.** north
   b. south   **e.** east or
   c. southwest   northeast
3. Answers will vary.

Page 18
1. Ensure the compass rose is correctly completed.
2. **a.** Ensure Hurricane Ridge is circled.
   b. southwest
3. northwest   6. west
4. south   7. north
5. southwest

Page 19
1. Ensure labels are correctly written on the map.
2. Answers will include four of the following: Eureka, San Francisco, San Diego, Acapulco, Salina Cruz
3. Caribbean Sea
4. Answers will include four of the following: Caracas, Paramaribo, Recife, Rio de Janeiro, Pôrto Alegre, Buenos Aires
5. Ensure the route is drawn in red to match the directions and that the cities are correctly circled.

Page 20
1. cardinal directions
2. North Pole; South Pole
3. intermediate directions
4. Directions; locations
5. Georgia
6. West Virginia
7. east
8. Arkansas; Louisiana

Page 21
Answers will vary.

Page 22
For questions 1–4, answers will vary.
5. Canada and Mexico

Page 23
1. Mexico City
2. United States
3. Baja California Norte, Sonora, Chihuahua, Coahuila, Tamaulipas
4. Jalisco, Michoacán

Page 24
1. Central America
2. Pan-American Highway
3. Mountain
4. north
5. El Salvador, Nicaragua, Costa Rica, Belize, Guatemala, Honduras, Panama
6. Mexico, Guatemala, El Salvador, Honduras, Nicaragua, Costa Rica, Panama, Colombia
7. **a.** Guatemala
   b. 13,845 and 13,045 feet
8. Cerro Pirre

Page 25
1. Panama
2. International boundary, National capital, Provincial capital, Mountain range, Pan-American Highway, Panama Canal
3. Ensure the compass rose is correctly labeled.
4. Ensure the bodies of water are correctly labeled.
5. Colombia
6. Costa Rica
7. three
8. Bocas del Toro, David, Penonomé, Santiago, Chitré, Las Tablas, Colón, Panama City, La Palma
9. south

Page 26
1. It is an international border.
2. Ensure that Regina is correctly circled.
3. Ensure that the border of Saskatchewan is traced.
   a. Alberta
   b. Manitoba
4. Ottawa
5. Nova Scotia
6. Nunavu
7. Yellowknife
8. Whitehorse

Page 27
1. Ensure the compass rose is correctly labeled.
2. **a.** Haiti, Port-au-Prince
   b. Dominican Republic, Santo Domingo
3. Cuba, Jamaica
4. **a.** northwest
   b. southeast
5. Caribbean Sea

Page 28
1. political map   7. E
2. title   8. A
3. boundaries   9. C
4. legend   10. F
5. symbol   11. D
6. B

Page 29
Answers will vary.

Page 30
1. Ensure that route is correctly drawn.
2. Atlantic Ocean, Gulf of St. Lawrence, St. Lawrence River, Lake Ontario, Welland Canal, Lake Erie, Detroit River, St. Clair River, Lake Huron, Lake Michigan, Illinois Drainage Canal, Illinois River
3. Québec, Montreal, Toronto, Buffalo, Cleveland, Detroit

Page 31
1. sea routes, railroads, Trans-Siberian Railroad, seaports, inland waterways
2. sea routes or the Trans-Siberian Railroad and other railroads
3. The Trans-Siberian Railroad

Page 32
1. **a.** goods/products
   b. A forklift will transport them to other places.
2. **a.** information/ideas
   b. The students are collecting information through using the computer and talking.

Maps: Read, Understand, Apply 5–6, SV9781419099434

Page 33
1. streets and train tracks
2. Answers should include three of the following: school, library, museum, and post office
3. Answers will vary.
4. The hospital worker should travel north on 12th Avenue and take a right on Circle Drive, heading east to the train station. The train station will be on the right side of the street.

Page 34
1. miles, kilometers
2. 400 miles

Page 35
1. 240 miles
2. 900 miles
3. Alaska is larger than Hawaii.
4. the United States map scale
5. 220 miles
6. No. The space between Honolulu and Los Angeles is not shown on the maps.

Page 36
1. the United States
2. 480 miles
3. Alaska, Hawaii
4. 960 miles
5. 240 miles
6. 1,200 miles
7. 1,000 miles
8. Portland to Chicago

Page 37
1. Ensure that Jefferson City is circled.
2. a. SW   3. a. W   4. a. SE
   b. 120   b. 60   b. 240
5. Ensure that Taum Sauk Mountain is correctly labeled.

Page 38
1. Libya
2. Ensure that all symbols in the legend and on the map are checked.
3. Ensure that compass rose is correctly labeled.
4. 280 MI; 450 KM
5. a. 150 KM; 70 MI
   b. 300 KM; 190 MI
   c. 300 KM; 190 MI
   d. 450 KM; 280 MI
6. Oil field #5 to Tobruk
7. to the coast. Answers may include: Oil can be transported on tankers; Cities on the coast may have industries or refineries.

Page 39
1. a. 1,300 KM; 800 MI
   b. 2,000 KM; 1,250 MI
   c. 1,000 KM; 650 MI
   d. 1,600 KM; 1,000 MI
   e. 400 KM; 300 MI
   f. 2,800 KM; 1,700 MI
   g. 1,600 KM; 1,000 MI
2. 10,700 KM; 6,700 MI
3. 1,700 KM; 1,100 MI
4. 1,400 KM; 900 MI
5. The Congo River trip is longer.

Page 40
1. map scale
2. miles (MI)
3. kilometers (KM)
4. inset map
5. 480
6. 360
7. 840
8. Nashville to Richmond

Page 41
Answers will vary.

Page 42
1. interstate highways, U.S. highways, state highways, scenic roads
2. Duluth, San Antonio
3. Highway 4

Page 43
1. Lake Superior, Lake Michigan, Lake Huron, Lake Erie
2. Pacific States, Southwest, Southeast
3. 1,122 miles
4. Interstate 15
5. U.S. 83
6. Interstates 90 and 15

Page 44
1. the Great Lakes States
2. U.S., state, interstate
3. Ensure the compass rose is correctly labeled.
4. Minnesota, Wisconsin, Illinois, Indiana, Michigan, Ohio
5. 29, I-94
6. 29, 51, 2
7. in Madison

Page 45
1. Springfield
2. Ensure that Chicago is circled.
3. 180
4. a. Interstate 55 through Normal
   b. southwest
5. a. 90   b. southwest
6. a. 80   b. northeast
7. about two hours

Page 46
1. the Mountain States
2. Montana, Idaho, Wyoming, Nevada, Utah, Colorado
3. a. Ensure Helena to Salt Lake City is traced in green.
   b. I-15
   c. 482
   d. Montana, Idaho, Utah
4. a. Ensure students have traced Helena to Cheyenne in orange.
   b. I-15, I-90, U.S. 89, U.S. 20, I-25
5. 95
6. in Las Vegas

Page 47
1. 139
2. a. 50
   b. about 45
   c. The highway curves.
3. a. about 55 KM
   b. 80 KM
4. a. Black Lake
   b. 20 and 265
5. a. 132
   b. Answers will vary.

Page 48
1. interstate highway
2. U.S. highway
3. mileage marker
4. state highway
5. region
6. interchange
7. I-35   8. I-10   9. U.S. 70
10. I-40, I-25, I-10, I-20

Page 49
Answers will vary.

Page 50
1. severe desertification
2. It is mostly none with moderate desertification.
3. Answers will vary.

Page 51
1. 1900 to present
2. the North Sea and some rivers
3. near Amsterdam and IJsselmeer
4. They have built canals.
5. Answers will vary.

Page 52
1. near Montreal, Lake Ontario, Lake Huron, Lake Erie, Lake Michigan, parts of Michigan, New York, Pennsylvania, West Virginia, Ohio, Indiana, Illinois, Kentucky, Chicago, Detroit, and Toronto
2. These areas have the least amounts of acid rain.
3. Answers will vary.

Page 53
1. all coastal areas of Mexico
2. in areas of little or no land use
3. Gulf of Mexico because of the oil there

Page 54
1. Pacific States, Mountain States, Great Lakes States, Plains States, Northwest
2. along the coastlines
3. the Northwestern Pacific coast
4. Pacific States, Southeast

Page 55
1. warm summers and cold winters
2. Alaska: cool summers, cold winters
3. cool summers, mild winters
4. Answers will vary.

Page 56
1. the population of the United States
2. Ensure that symbols are correctly added to the legend.
3. Chicago, Philadelphia, Los Angeles, or Dallas
4. New York City
5. Under 2 people per square mile
6. eastern

Page 57
1. explorers of North America
2. Ensure the intermediate directions are correctly labeled on the compass rose.
3. Ensure pattern for Columbus is correctly drawn.
4. Spain
5. a. Hudson
   b. the Netherlands
   c. 1609 and 1610
   d. Hudson Bay or Hudson River
6. Ensure DeSoto's route is traced in red; Mississippi River
7. Ensure Coronado's route is traced in blue; Mexico
8. Spain   9. southern

Page 58
1. Europe   4. ferns and vines
2. I   5. North America
3. weaver birds

Page 59
1. land use in the Plains States
2. farmland
3. North Dakota
4. Iowa and Nebraska
5. grazing land
6. south
7. a. Ensure that Kansas City and St. Louis are circled.
   b. Kansas City, St. Louis
   c. about 225 miles

Page 60
1. population map
2. special purpose map
3. resource map
4. symbol
5. Arizona and New Mexico
6. Texas
7. Beef cattle, sheep, fruit, or oil
8. Arizona
9. Arizona and New Mexico

Page 61
Answers will vary.

Page 62
1. Chinatown, Afro-American Museum, or Pennsylvania Convention Center
2. Independence Hall
3. Fairmount Park
4. B-2

Maps: Read, Understand, Apply 5–6, SV9781419099434

5. Delaware River
6. I-76, I-676

Page 63
1. D-2
2. Courthouse
3. a. B-4   b. northeast
4. A-1, A-2
5. a. E-4
   b. Tower of the Americas, Alamodome

Page 64
1. Washington, D.C.
2. Ensure the compass rose is correctly labeled.
3. Ensure that grid is correctly completed.
4. a. B-2
   b. Ensure that the White House is circled.
5. a. C-2
   b. Ensure that the Washington Monument is circled.
6. a. Thomas Jefferson Memorial
   b. Lincoln Memorial or Vietnam Veterans Memorial
7. a. C-5
   b. Supreme Court and Library of Congress
8. National Gallery of Art

Page 65
1. a. Theatre of Performing Arts, Municipal Auditorium
   b. N. Rampart Street
2. a. Cabrini Doll Museum, Preservation Hall, Pharmacy Museum, International Trade Mart
   b. St. Philip St., Bourbon St.
3. The three places are circled in red on the map.
   a. D-7   b. D-6   c. F-2
4. French Market, Café du Monde, Pharmacy Museum
5. Burgundy Street

Page 66
1. a. A-1
   b. Ensure that the Maritime Museum is circled in red.
2. a. B-2
   b. Ensure that the Cable Car Museum is circled in blue.
3. northwest   5. Interstate 80
4. east   6. U.S. 101

Page 67
1. a. B-6, C-6
   b. First Avenue
2. a. C-1 and C-2
   b. Ensure the route from United Nations Headquarters to Times Square is traced.
   c. Answers may include: Chrysler Building, Grand Central Station, Public Library

3. a. B-2
   b. Ensure the route from Times Square to Radio City Music Hall is traced.
   c. Avenue of the Americas
4. a. E-3
   b. Ensure that the route from Radio City Music Hall east to Fifth Avenue is traced.
   c. Ensure that the route to the Empire State Building is traced.
   d. 34th Street

Page 68
1. grid
2. coordinate
3. map index
4. Ensure that the grid is correctly labeled.
5. C-5
6. B-6
7. northeast
8. D-7
9. southeast
10. E-6

Page 69
Answers will vary.

Page 70
1. Each is located along or near water.
2. about 700 miles
3. Vancouver, Seattle, Portland

Page 71
1. Ensure the Garden District is correctly labeled on the map.
2. The neighborhood has a view of Lake Pontchartrain.
3. Answers may include: French culture or style would be found there in homes and buildings, in food, and more.
4. Answers will vary.

Page 72
1. physical feature
2. Antarctica
3. central South America
4. Answers may include: Since plains are flatter than mountains, they are more easily settled and farmed than are mountains. This would create larger populations. There may be differences in climate or temperature.

Page 73
1. human feature
2. Christianity
3. Asia
4. Europe, the Middle East, United States, and Eastern Russia
5. Answers will vary.

Page 74
1. Quito, Bogotá, Accra, Mogadishu, Padang
2. New Orleans, Cairo, Baghdad
3. Brasília, Mozambique
4. London, Accra

5. Baghdad, Mogadishu
6. Montreal, Bogotá, Quito

Page 75
1. Ensure the cities are correctly labeled.
2. a. 52°N, 8°E
   b. 52°N, 12°E
   c. 49°N, 9°E

Page 76
1. west
2. Western Hemisphere
3. a. Ensure the 150°W meridian is traced in green.
   b. Anchorage
4. a. Ensure the 120°W meridian is traced in red.
   b. Reno
5. a. Ensure the 80°W meridian is traced in orange.
   b. Buffalo
6. a. Ensure that Lima is circled.
   b. 75°W
7. a. Ensure that Sucre is circled.
   b. 65°W
8. Boston

Page 77
1. Quito
2. Havana
3. São Paulo
4. Santiago de Cuba
5. Panama City
6. 15°N or 16°N
7. 6°N
8. 34°S or 35°S
9. Pôrto Alegre
10. 12°S

Page 78
1. a. Ensure the 70°W meridian is traced in green.
   b. west
   c. the Western Hemisphere
2. a. Ensure the Equator is traced in red.
   b. Check that "N" is written north of the Equator.
   c. Check that "S" is written south of the Equator.
3. a. Mitú   b. 0°
4. a. 90°W   d. 85°W
   b. 20°S   e. 10°S
   c. 40°N   f. 55°W

Page 79
1. Ensure that all points are correctly labeled.
2. a. NW   c. NW
   b. W   d. NE
3. Atlantic Ocean
4. Gulf of Mexico
5. Bahamas, Florida, and Louisiana

Page 80
1. Prime Meridian
2. parallels
3. meridians

4. a. Springfield
   b. Philadelphia
   c. Boulder
   d. Memphis
5. a. 30°N, 90°W
   b. 40°N, 80°W
   c. 40°N, 120°W
   d. 30°N, 95°W

Page 81
Answers will vary.

Page 83
1. because it is found near the poles
2. Answers will vary.

Page 84
1. Ensure that zones on map are correctly labeled. Frigid Zone and Temperate Zone should be used twice.
2. Ensure that zones are colored according to directions.
3. a. Frigid Zone, high
   b. Temperate Zone, middle
   c. Temperate Zone, middle
   d. Torrid Zone, low
   e. Temperate Zone, middle
   f. Torrid Zone, low
   g. Temperate Zone, middle
   h. Torrid Zone, low
   i. Torrid Zone, low

Page 85
1. Ankara
2. Mediterranean climate
3. Steppe climate
4. cold and dry
5. hot and dry
6. Mediterranean climate
7. Mt. Ararat has cold, dry winters while Mt. Olympus has cool, rainy winters.
8. Turkey's eastern border has a hot and dry climate most of the year with cold, dry winters.

Page 86
1. a. Singapore, Panama City, Accra
   b. Las Vegas, Aswan, Alice Springs
   c. Buenos Aires, Charleston, Athens, Shanghai
   d. Anchorage, Stockholm, Moscow, Yakutsk
   e. Barrow, Eismitte, Murmansk
   f. Chengdu, La Paz, Banff
2. Polar
3. Torrid Zone
4. the Northern Hemisphere

Page 87
1. the climate of Europe
2. cold temperate
3. a. Helsinki, cold temperate
   b. Volgograd, dry
   c. Bergen, mild temperate
   d. Belgrade, cold temperate
   e. Dublin, mild temperate

Maps: Read, Understand, Apply 5–6, SV9781419099434

4. a. 60ºN, 30ºE, cold
temperate
b. 50ºN, 30ºE, cold
temperate
c. 50ºN, 0º, mild temperate
d. 40ºN, 50ºE, dry
e. 40ºN, 5ºW, mild
temperate
5. 60ºN

Page 88
1. middle latitudes
2. low latitudes, Torrid Zone
3. Frigid Zone
4. climate
5. **a.** Madras, Bangkok,
Singapore
b. Chimbai, Qitai, Balkhash
c. Guangzhou, Taipei,
Tokyo
d. Omsk, Irkutsk, Seoul
e. Dickson, Nordvik,
Ambarchik
f. Konduz, Gar, Lhasa

Page 89
Answers will vary.

Page 90
1. Answers will vary.
2. The zone borders the Pacific
Ocean.
3. Rocky Mountains
4. Eastern

Page 91
1. 5   4. 7
2. west   5. west
3. 7:00 A.M.   6. 1:00 A.M.

Page 92
1. Ensure that time zones are
colored to match directions.
2. **a.** Pacific   **d.** Hawaii-
b. Central   Aleutian
c. Eastern
3. 11:00 A.M.   6. 3:00 P.M.
4. 1:00 P.M.   7. 11:00 P.M.
5. 1:00 P.M.   8. 3:30 A.M.

Page 93
1. northwest
2. 3:00 P.M.
3. Ensure that line is drawn
according to directions.
4. 850
5. west
6. Ensure that line is drawn
according to directions.
7. 8:00 A.M.
8. 10:00 A.M.

Page 94
1. Ensure that times zones are
colored to match directions.
2. Ensure that clocks above
map are correctly labeled.
3. **a.** 8:00 A.M.   **e.** 11:00 A.M.
b. 10:00 A.M.   **f.** 9:00 A.M.
c. 6:00 A.M.   **g.** 11:00 A.M.
d. 7:00 A.M.   **h.** 12:00 noon
4. **a.** 6:00 P.M.   **d.** 4:00 P.M.
b. 5:00 P.M.   **e.** 3:00 P.M.
c. 2:00 P.M.   **f.** 1:00 P.M.

Page 95
1. 12:01 A.M. Tuesday
2. **a.** four
b. three
3. one
4. four or five, depending on
the route taken
5. four
6. 3:00 P.M.
7. 10:00 A.M.
8. ahead, four
9. ahead 9 hours

Page 96
1. standard time zones
2. International Date Line
3. Central 4. Pacific 5. Eastern
6. **a.** 6:00 P.M.   **d.** 9:00 P.M.
b. 8:00 P.M.   **e.** 7:00 P.M.
c. 4:00 P.M.   **f.** 5:00 P.M.

Page 97
Answers will vary.

Page 98
1. Ensure Greenland is
correctly labeled on the
map.
For questions 2–3, ensure that
locations are correctly labeled
on the map.
4. Mexico is south of the
United States, between the
Pacific Ocean and the Gulf
of Mexico.

Page 99
1. It is on one of the middle
islands, which would make
its location as the capital
central to the rest of the
islands.
2. Estimate: 20ºN, 155ºW
3. Near the ocean, along the
coast. Answers will vary.

Page 101
For questions 1–3, ensure that
cities are correctly labeled on
the map.
2. Bolivia
4. Ensure Mt. Aconcagua is
correctly circled on the map.
5. **a.** Bogotá   **c.** Asunción
b. Sucre   **d.** Paramaribo
6. The Amazon River
is located in northern
Brazil, from the Atlantic
Ocean west to the Andes
Mountains.
7. 14ºS, 56ºW
8. Uruguay
9. 16ºS, 48ºW
10. Guyana is located in
northern South America.
It is north of Brazil, east
of Venezuela, west of
Suriname, and south of the
Caribbean Sea.

Pages 102–103
1. c   2. c   3. b   4. a
5. Interstate Highway 695
6. Interstate Highway 195 to
State Highway 256
7. d   8. b   9. a   10. d
11. 900 tons
12. less than 10 inches

Maps: Read, Understand, Apply 5–6, SV9781419099434